D0407460

A GEOGRAPHY OF minerals

Geography is one of man's oldest sciences, yet it is as new as the Space Age. Knowledge of the earth obtained from satellite photography and measurement, remote sensing of the environment, and by means of other sophisticated techniques are really but a stage in the evolutionary process that began with ancient man's curiosity about his surroundings. Man has always been interested in the earth and the things on it. Today this interest may be channeled through the discipline of geography, which offers one means of organizing a vast amount of physical and cultural information.

The **Brown Foundations of Geography Series** has been created to facilitate the study of physical, cultural, and methodological geography at the college level. The **Series** is a carefully selected group of titles that covers the wide spectrum of basic geography. While the individual titles are self-contained, collectively they comprise a modern synthesis of major geographical principles. The underlying theme of each book is to foster an awareness of geography as an imaginative, evolving science.

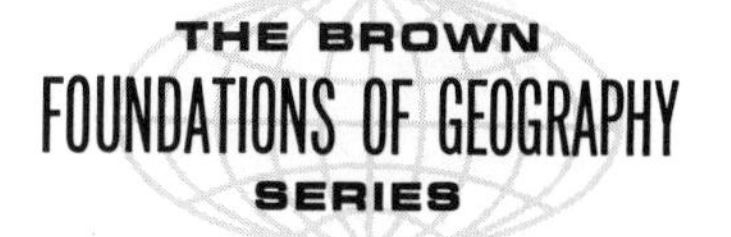

7UVC

A GEOGRAPHY OF minerals

WALTER H. VOSKUIL
University of Nevada

WM. C. BROWN COMPANY PUBLISHERS
DUBUQUE, IOWA

THE BROWN
FOUNDATIONS OF GEOGRAPHY
SERIES

Consulting Editor
ROBERT H. FUSON
University of South Florida

Library of Congress Catalog Card Number: 69-10383

Printed in the United States of America

Preface

Mineral resources are located randomly by nature. Some kinds of minerals are so widely distributed that nearly all countries have adequate supplies within their boundaries or near at hand. Other minerals are so distributed that some countries have more than they need and others do not have enough. No country is self-sufficient in regard to either resources or markets for all minerals.

The history of industrial development shows that only a few localities in the world have the right combinations of mineral supplies to favor establishment of industries. These industrial districts must necessarily buy some of the minerals they need from remote quarters of the globe. Thus the geographic distribution of minerals leads inevitably to international trade in minerals. In order to cut the high cost of transporting bulky raw materials, however, it is important to concentrate, refine, and fabricate them as near to the source of supply as possible.

The core of the mineral productive pattern is the iron-ore and fuel group of minerals. If a society is to be highly productive, it must be lavishly equipped with power-driven machinery, which means it must have abundant supplies of iron. Iron therefore assumes a major role among the metals; in fact, iron accounts for nine-tenths of all metal used. But iron is a product of iron ore and fuel—a special fuel. The coke used to process the iron ore is made from high-quality coal, and coking coal is restricted in distribution. About one-fourth of the total fuels used in all manufacturing is used in this first step of converting iron ore into pig iron. The great tonnages and the special quality of fuel needed tend to localize pig iron production at points where the sum of transportation costs of ore, fuel, and finished product to market are lowest.

The ferroalloys comprise a group of metals which, added to iron, change the properties of the resulting steel in various ways. Manganese, chromium, nickel, molybdenum, tungsten, and vanadium are used primarily as alloy materials in making steel. Aluminum and copper, as alloys, give steel certain important properties, but these metals are important in their own right.

The nonferrous metals include aluminum, copper, lead, magnesium, zinc, and tin. Their usefulness is based upon their particular properties and their role in special nonferrous alloys. Copper, as the most efficient low-priced conductor of electricity, is the basis of the electrical industry. Lead, the most widely used metal for cable coverings, cooperates with copper in conducting electricity through oceanic cables. In these and many other ways the nonferrous metals function with steel as vital agents of production.

The light metals are aluminum, magnesium, and titanium. Their ores are abundant in nature. These metals have aroused much interest because of high public expectations regarding their possibilities in consumer goods as well as productive machinery.

Minerals of construction include asbestos, asphalt, cement, clays, sand and gravel, sandstone, gypsum, lime, slate, and stone. The multiplicity of building requirements calls for a great variety of minerals, which are needed in enormous tonnages every year for industrial structures to house the machinery of production, for factories and office buildings, and for extensive transportation facilities.

Chemical minerals include a wide variety of minor metals and minerals which have limited or special functions. One such group is the fertilizer group—nitrate, phosphate, potash, and sulfur—which contributes chiefly by increasing agricultural crop production.

The basic pattern of mineral economy has not changed much since man first developed a process of producing iron and steel cheaply. The rise of the light-metal industry has added to the list of industrial raw materials that compete in some degree with iron, copper, lead, and tin. However, new materials have not altered the pattern of production set by steel, nor is any major change probable. Neither is there apt to be any radical change in power supply in the immediate future, in spite of developments in nuclear physics and the release of nuclear power.

Political factors come into the industrial picture because the minerals needed by industry are under divided political control. The world industrial pattern is such that minerals flow into a few centers for processing and manufacture. Nations outside of the industrial centers function as suppliers of mineral raw materials.

Out of this economic relationship various political situations arise. Minerals necessary to the manufacture of steel become the object of rivalry among industrial powers. Nations that own mineral resources may set up tariffs and export or license fees; they may restrict the right to explore or develop their resources; and they frequently make special trade agreements in order to drive bargains with the nations that must buy the minerals.

The need among nations for cooperation, based on comprehensive and continued research, is self-evident. In one area of human need alone, that of increasing the world's food supply, the use of minerals will play and expanding role by providing plant food for the soil, chemicals to protect the growing plant, and machines to increase man's efficiency in producing the food.

It is not possible to acknowledge briefly all sources of information which have been helpful in compiling the data presented in this volume, but the more important works of reference are cited in the bibliography at the end of the text. Publications of the American Iron and Steel Institute, the American Institute of Mining and Metallurgical Engineers, the American Petroleum Institute, the U.S. Bureau of Mines, the U.S. Geological Survey, the Illinois State Geological Survey, and the U.S. Census Bureau are especially prolific sources of information that have been used freely.

Contents

Chapter 1

Introductory Statement

A mineral geography survey portrays only the known deposits, and among these, only such as are of distinct economic significance. A mineral geography, at best, can only be tentative, since discoveries are continuing and, we believe, will continue to occur in the forseeable future. As here conceived, mineral geography does not include an exhaustive cataloging of every reported deposit many of which play only a minor role in the world's economy.

Economic Valuation of a Mineral Deposit

A mineral deposit must be evaluated in terms of its usefulness to one or more of the several industrial complexes of the world. These complexes or industrial districts are firmly established in northern and eastern United States, in northwestern continental Europe, the United Kingdom, in the U.S.S.R., in Japan, and in Italy. There are distinct possibilities in China and India. Other industrial developments in existence, or likely to arise, are of minor significance.

Nearly all producible ores, or the concentrated or refined products of such ores, will seek a market in one or more of the industrial complexes. The value of an ore body will be governed by the quality and size of the deposit and accessibility to market. In the majority of cases, ores that have recently been discovered are also far removed from industrial centers. The characteristics of an ore body that bring it into the sphere of commercial availability usually are a combination of high quality, in physical form and metal content, a large deposit, and acessibility to ocean transportation.

Ore Reserves and Modern Ocean Transportation

Several ore bodies, both those newly discovered and otherwise, have entered the lists of favored commercial ore bodies or mineral deposits because of the drastically changed conditions in the cost of ocean transportation, especially since the close of World War II. The attractiveness of these ore bodies for purposes of commercial exploitation originally stemmed from their size and quality, and tidewater location.

The favorably located ores in or near the industrial complexes were showing signs of decline or exhaustion during the post-war period, entailing a need for alternative sources of metal. The compelling factor was the evolution of the large carrier and the accompanying reduction in shipping costs. At the close of World War II, a 15,000-ton freighter was a fairly large sized carrier. The vessels of today are represented by tankers of 240,000 ton capacity, and iron ore carriers approaching 100,000 tons. Colliers of 70,000 tons capacity carry coal from Hampton Roads, Virginia, to Rotterdam, and lay down American coal at delivered costs that are competitive with mine price coal in the Ruhr.

Ore Reserves and Changing Technology

The provisional nature of estimated ore reserves and location of ore bodies is illustrated by the increasing efficiency in ore recovery. As an example, the average grade of copper ore in the United States declined from 2.0 per cent in 1946 to 0.8 per cent in 1966. This decline in grade of minable ore has been accompanied by a delineation of hitherto unidentified ore bodies. With improving ore recovery practices, not to mention the possibility of price increases, extending the realm of possible ore bodies, it follows that future discoveries will add to the list of ore resources and modify present day concepts of mineral geography.

Some nations have one, or at the most only a limited number, of mineral resources. Clearly many countries do not have the array of basic ores and fuels essential for the development of an industrial complex. These nations are limited to the sale and export abroad of minerals as ores or to initial steps in concentration or preparation of metals in primary form. The foreign exchange available to a raw material exporting nation is meager in comparison to the manufactured goods that are sought through imports.

Order of Presentation

In the order of presentation of the minerals, iron is given first place because of its predominant position as an industrial raw material and the basis of a productive economy. The use of fuels and power pervade all aspects of the economy from household chores to the heavy demands of metal smelting and fabrication, the chemical and ceramic industries, and the varied forms of transportation. The nonferrous metals; copper, lead, zinc and aluminum, all occupy important and indispensable roles in the industrial complex so characteristic of the western world that they are considered immediately after the iron and fuel groups.

Building materials, in all their variety, are handmaidens of industrial society, and, tonnagewise, are the most important group of raw materials. Increasing awareness of the need for an expanded food supply is focusing attention on the mineral raw materials essential in the production of fertilizer materials. This subject is discussed in a final chapter.

Chapter **2**

Iron Ores

The iron ore deposits of the world may be classified into four groups:

1. Deposit with a long mining history and stabilized or declining output
2. Recently developed deposits
3. Inactive or dormant deposits
4. Very recent discoveries

The following characteristics of an ore body are used in the evaluation.

1. Grade
2. Size or estimated reserve
3. Physical qualities of the ore
4. Pelletizing or other beneficiating installations present
5. Transport facilities
6. Market connections
7. Competitive ore bodies

Ore Bodies in North America

the United States

Four distinct iron ore mining districts or regions are recognized in the United States: the Lake Superior district, the northeastern states, Alabama, and the western states.

The *Lake Superior* region is the most important source of iron ore in the United States. There are seven mining districts, of which the most important is the Mesabi. These ore bodies are formed over hundreds of square miles in northeastern Minnesota, in northern Wisconsin,

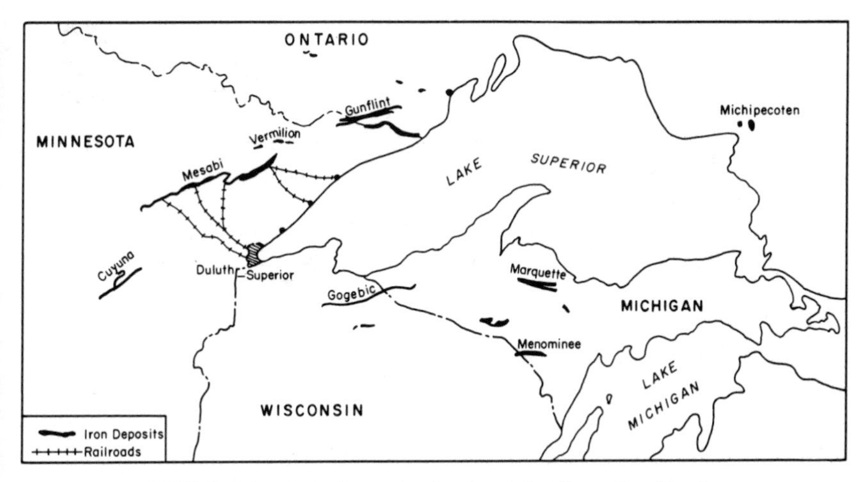

FIGURE 2.1 Iron Deposits in the Lake Superior District

and the Upper Peninsula of Michigan. Lake Superior ores have been remarkable for their uniformity over long periods, but even so the average grade of shipping ore is declining. Direct shipping ore[1] now accounts for about 25 per cent of the usable ore produced in the Lake Superior district, and the remainder consists of agglomerates and concentrates.

Taconite

Of long range importance to a continued iron ore industry in the Lake Superior district, particularly Minnesota, are the vast tonnages of taconite. The reserves have been estimated at 60,000 million tons.[2] This iron-silica rock, in its original form, contains 30-35 per cent iron. Before 1940, these were not considered to be workable ores, but at the close of World War II, several of the large steel corporations began to carry on intensive research on deposits of this type in the Mesabi Range of the Lake Superior region.

Most of the taconite ores contain iron in the form of hematite. However, at the eastern end of the Mesabi Range an intrusion of igneous rock has reduced the hematite to magnetite, suitable for separation by magnetic methods. The quantity of this magnetic taconite is estimated at 5000 million tons.

---

[1] "Direct shipping ore" is the term used for ores that are shipped from the mine without further beneficiation.

[2] Percival, F. G., The World's Iron Ore Supplies, 1959, British Iron and Steel Federation, London.

The Northeastern States. The Middle Atlantic region, comprising New Jersey, New York, and Pennsylvania, is probably the oldest continuous producer of iron ore in the United States. Together they produce about 5 million tons of usable ore, which are used by the local iron industry. In New York, magnetite is produced in both underground mines and open cut operations in Essex and Clinton counties. The output in Pennsylvania consists of magnetite from underground mines.

The *Birmingham* district in Alabama was founded on the unique location of vast quantities of iron ore, coking coal, and fluxing stone in close proximity. For many years the cost of making pig iron and steel in the Birmingham district has been the lowest in the country. All the raw materials were assembled at low cost of transportation. Direct shipping ore has decreased sharply in recent years and costs have risen. Consumption of iron ore in agglomerate plants and blast furnaces is about 40 per cent domestic ore and 60 per cent imports, received mainly from Venezuela and Chile.

In the *western states* ore bodies have been located and developed at Sunrise and Atlantic City, Wyoming; Cedar City, Utah; Douglas, Eureka and Pershing counties, Nevada; Riverside county, California; and Pitkin county, Colorado.

The output of the Atlantic City mine is shipped to the Geneva Steel plant in Utah, and the output of the Sunrise mine is shipped to Pueblo, Colorado. The principal soure of iron ore in California is the Eagle Mountain mine in Riverside county. The ore is shipped to the blast furnaces at Fontana. Pellets are also produced for shipment to the Japanese market. This is the largest iron ore operation in western United States.

In *southeast Missouri* the discovery and development of iron ore deposits at Pea Ridge (near Sullivan) and at Pilot Knob have brought about an iron ore output of significant usefulness to local steel industries. The mine output at Pea Ridge is processed into high grade pellets for shipment to Bethlehem Steel Corp. at Johnstown, Pa., Armo Steel Corp., Hamilton, Ohio, and Lone Star Steel Company at Daingerfield, Texas. At full capacity, the five pelletizing furnaces can produce 2 million tons of iron pellets containing about 68 per cent iron.

At Pilot Knob, the Pilot Knob Pellet Co. is equipped to produce 1 million tons of high grade pellets annually for shipment to the Granite City Steel plant, adjacent to East St. Louis, Illinois.

Canada

In 1963 Canada became the leading nation in the world in the tonnage of ore sold in the international iron ore market. From an output of less than 5 million long tons in 1950, production rose to 35 million long tons in 1964. The principal customer is the United States, but West Germany, the United Kingdom, and Japan also import considerable

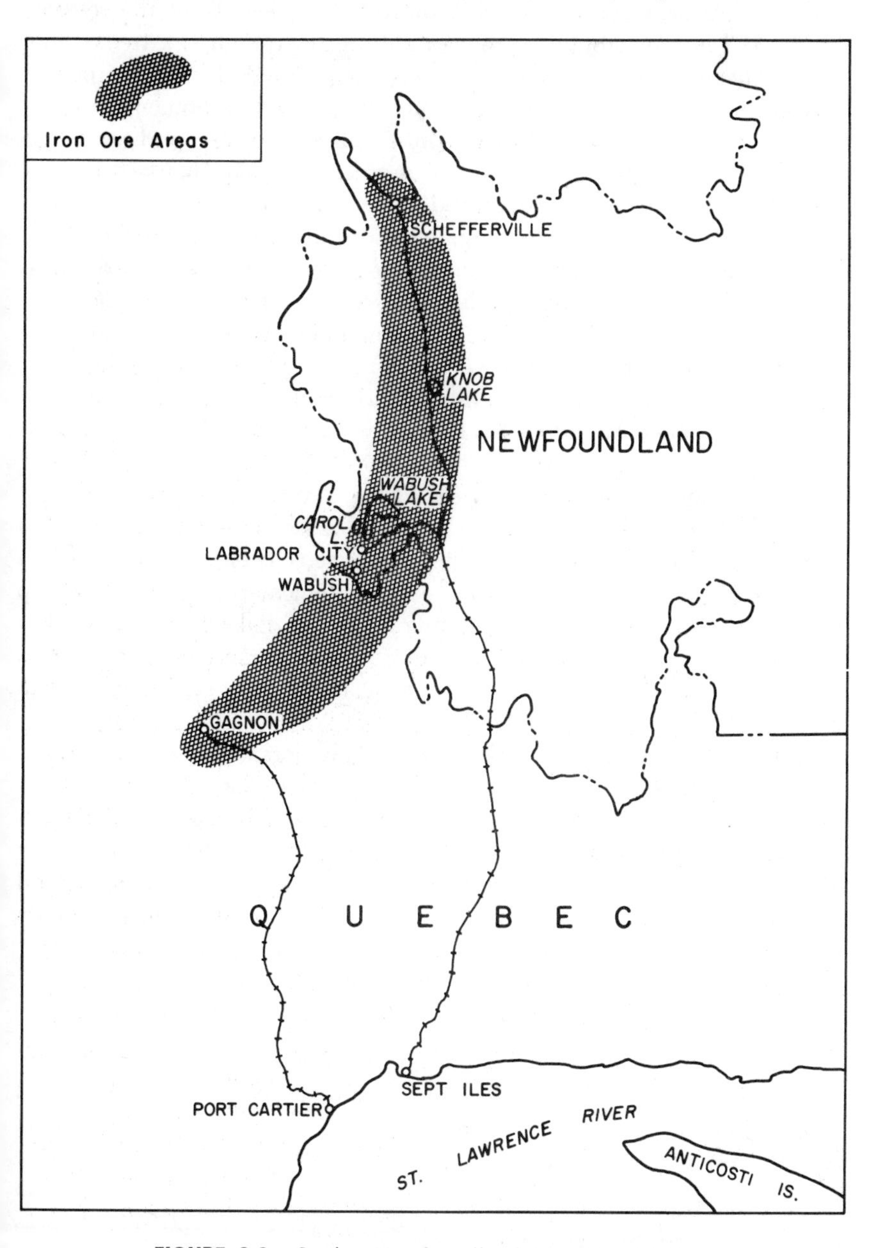

FIGURE 2.2 Quebec-Newfoundland Iron Ore District

quantities. The three principal sources of iron ore are the Quebec-Labrador region, the northern shore of the Great Lakes, and the coast of British Columbia.

Much of the recent increase in output and the bulk of the reserves are located in the Labrador Trough. Within this trough is a tremendous reserve of iron ore and exploration has disclosed a number of important producing mines which are in process of development.

Ore is transported over a 360-mile railway to the port of Seven Islands and thence by lake or ocean vessels. The main markets are the United States, United Kingdom and West Germany.

Quebec Cartier Mining Company is operating a mine at Lac Jeannine, at the south end of the Labrador Trough. The grade of ore is about 30 per cent and, before shipment, is concentrated to 66 per cent iron content. It is shipped 193 miles by rail to the all-year shipping port of Port Cartier.

The loading facilities at Seven Islands and the new dock at Port Cartier, both on the Gulf of St. Lawrence, are designed to load vessels up to 100,000 tons capacity.

On the north shore of the Great Lakes, ore deposits of Canada are divided roughly between those adjacent to Lake Superior and those in southeastern Ontario and southwestern Quebec. The Lake Superior group includes Steep Rock Lake, Nakina, and Michipicoten ranges. The Steep Rock iron deposit is located 140 miles west of Lake Superior at Port Arthur. The ores, as shipped, contain 56 to 59 per cent iron. Reserves of Steep Rock ore have been estimated to be approximately 250 million gross tons.

The Wabana mines on Bell Island in Conception Bay are an underground operation. These mines have been active since 1895 and, after beneficiation, yield a shipping product of 50 per cent iron content. The ore is exported mainly to the United Kingdom and West Germany.

In British Columbia, a number of small mines on Vancouver and Queen Charlotte Islands export between 1 and 2 million tons annually to Japan.

Mexico

Mexico possesses a number of iron ore deposits which provide ore for the local steel industry. The bulk of Mexican iron ore production comes from the Cerro de Mercado deposit near the city of Durango, and from a group of small mines in Coahuila and Nuevo León. The Cerro de Mercado deposit is the most important, both in production and reserves. The ore contains 63 to 65 per cent iron and the reserves are estimated at 60 million to 100 million tons.

Iron Ores in South America

South America is essentially a raw material producing and exporting continent. Processing and manufacturing have made only limited headway. Among the raw materials that move in important tonnages in international commerce are petroleum, iron ore, copper, and nitrogen.

The ore-producing nations in South America are participating in the overseas shipments of iron ores to ore-using centers in Western and Mediterranean Europe, in the United States, and in Japan. Brazil, Chile, Peru and Venezuela all participate in these markets. In 11 years (1951-1963) exports of iron ore rose from 4½ million long tons to nearly 40 million tons.

The development of big ships for ore has resulted in more tonnage outlets for Latin American mines; it has not necessarily increased the returns per ton, or even for an individual country. More ore is being sold, but more mines are being opened, also. Nor has it resulted in a significant increase in smelting and fabricating industries, although beginnings are being made. This growth in exports has materialized in spite of the fact that competition in the world iron ore market among producing districts, new and old, is very keen.

In this world market, the South American countries suffer certain disadvantages, such as long distance from markets, or long inland rail hauls, or both. These competitive relationships have been changing constantly with each new ore development elsewhere, and changes may be expected in future years.

Venezuela

The most favored nation in the South American group is Venezuela. This nation began producing and shipping ore about 1950 and now exports more than twice as much as Brazil.

The known and commercially active iron ore deposits of Venezuela lie on both sides of the Caroní River, south of the Orinoco River. Cerro Bolívar is the larger and more important of these two deposits. Overall average iron content is about 62 per cent. Orinoco Mining Company, (a subsidiary of U.S. Steel Corp.) began operations in 1954 and does its shipping from Puerto Ordaz on the Orinoco. The Iron Mines Company of Venezuela began operations in 1950 at El Pao and ships from Palua, also on the Orinoco. Production of the two operations reached a high of 19 million long tons in 1960 but has since declined to about 10 million long tons. The downward trend in production has been attributed to severe competition from Canadian exports to the United States, and the difficulty of Venezuelan ores, which carry a high percentage of fines, in meeting competition from iron ore pellets. Venezuela exports most of its output to the United States but also ships quantities to the United Kingdom, West Germany and Italy. The Cerro Bolívar and El Pao deposits are credited with a proven reserve of 730 million metric tons. The total Venezuelan iron ore reserve at the beginning of 1963 was estimated at over 2 billion metric tons of which 1.3 billion is proven ore and the remainder is probable. The average grade is 50 per cent.

Chile

Iron ore has become Chile's most important mineral export next to copper. About four-fifths of the iron ore output is exported and the remainder is processed into iron and steel in Chile's domestic industry. More than 90 per cent of the iron and steel output is accounted for by the Compania de Acero del Pacifico. This firm is a highly integrated steel company located at Huachipato.

Most of the high grade iron ore deposits are in southern Atacama and northern Coquimbo provinces, in a well-defined belt, inland from the Pacific Coast and extending from Taltal to Ovalle. Reserves in the area are estimated at 180 million tons of high grade ore. The two largest ore bodies within this belt are at El Romeral and Algarrobo. The El Romeral deposit is about 15 miles north of Serena. The Algarrobo deposit is located about 20 miles southwest of Vallenar, and a similar distance southeast of Huasco. The largest known deposit in Chile is the El Loco in this latter province. The reserve is estimated at from 100 to 150 million metric tons. The deposit is located at an elevation of 15,000 feet, 200 miles from the coast.

The two principal importers of Chilean ore are the United States and Japan. Additional small quantities go to Western Europe. Vessels transporting ore from Chile and Peru to the eastern United States and Europe are limited to about 40,000 tons DWT by the dimensions of the Panama Canal. Chilean iron ore ports of Chanaral and Caldera have been deepened and loading facilities modernized to accomodate larger vessels such as the 51,000 ton ore carrier of the Japanese fleet.

Peru

The Marcona Mining Company is the largest iron ore company in Peru. The ore deposit operated by this company has a known reserve of 400 million tons, and lies about 210 miles south of Lima. By selective mining, the producer is able to maintain a uniform grade of 60 to 61 per cent ore. A plant has been constructed to produce pellets which assay 68 to 69 per cent iron.

The principal outlets for Peruvian ores are Japan, the United States, and West Germany. Minor quantities are shipped to several other west European nations. An ore carrier of 91,000 tons DWT has been built in Japan to carry iron ore from operations of the Marcona Mining Company to steel mill customers in Japan.

The Marcona mine and ore beneficiation facilities are located on the arid coast of Peru, 250 miles south of the capital of Lima. The ore is shipped from a deep water port at San Nicolas Bay. This port is equipped with facilities to load ships of more than 100,000 DWT.

Brazil

Large reserves of high-grade iron ore are reported to exist in nearly every state but mining is confined principally to Minas Gerais. Recently limited production is occurring in Mato Grosso and Paraná. The total iron reserve of the country has been estimated at 42 billion tons, but a large fraction of this figure represents material that has little economic significance because of its low grade, physical nature, or remote location. The indicated reserves of high grade hematite of 66 per cent or higher iron content in Minas Gerais total more than 3300 million tons, and are among the largest in the world. The bulk of the iron ore output comes from these deposits.

The Compania Vale de Rio Doce accounts for 80 per cent of the iron ore expected from Brazil. In addition to its mines on Caue Peak, the company owns the railroad, 300 miles in length, to the port of Vitoria. The CVRD has completed in 1960 a new ore terminal with facilities to permit the export of 15 million tons annually. This port can accomodate vessels of 100,000 tons DWT. The new port also includes facilities to transship coal destined for steel mills in the Rio Doce Valley.

The problem of Brazil in the international iron ore market is one of transportation costs. She has a rail haul of about 300 miles from mine to port and a sea voyage far in excess of her most active competitors. Brazil's principal competitors are Venezuela, West Afrcian producers, Sweden, and Canada.

The future for Latin American ore exports is somewhat uncertain in a continuously changing world competitive situation. Ore bodies of large size and high grade near tidewater in West Africa and Canada threaten the Brazilian markets in Western Europe and the United States. In Japan, the market is under pressure from the newly exploited ore bodies in Australia, not to mention the existing ore producers in Malaya and India.

Raw Materials and South America's Problems of Industrial Development

The achievements in low-cost ocean transportation, which have been instrumental in establishing steel industries in hitherto minor steel-producing nations, has not had a comparable result in South America. Whereas Italy and Japan, both among the majors, have a background of industrial experience coupled with a foreign trade based on high-valued manufactured goods, South America must rely for foreign exchange mainly on low-valued raw materials.

The Iron Ores of Europe

The continent of Europe possesses extensive iron ore deposits of relatively medium and low grade; however, the annual ore output falls below the annual consumption. Imports from abroad are substantial and increasing. The principal foreign suppliers of ore for the European market are the mining countries of western and northern Africa, Venezuela, Brazil, Peru and Canada. Small quantities are imported from India.

Eight Western European nations account for nearly 90 per cent of the iron ore output of the area. These are France, Sweden, United Kingdom, West Germany, Luxembourg and Spain. As stated above, the iron content of European ores is generally low. The exceptions are Sweden, the second largest producer, and Spain with a limited output. The reported grade of ore for each of these nations is as follows:

	Per cent iron
France	30
Sweden	61
United Kingdom	28
West Germany	27
Luxembourg	30
Spain	50

The weighted average iron content of all European production is 37 per cent.

France

France ranks first among the nations of Western Europe as an iron ore producer and third in the world. She accounts for three-fourths of the iron output of the European Coal and Steel Community. The principal ore deposits are in the Lorraine Basin; there are also sizable deposits in Normandy, Brittany, and Anjou. The Lorraine deposits lie in eastern France in the departments of Muerthe-et-Moselle and Lorraine and extend northward into Luxembourg.

As the Lorraine ores contain much phosphorus, they were not used extensively until after 1878 when Thomas and Gilchrist discovered a method of converting high phosphorus pig iron into steel. After that the value of the Lorraine "minette" ores increased substantially. Currently the ore output has met all the requirements of the steel industry in eastern France and of the Saar area's steel industry of western Germany, as well as a portion of the ore requirements of Belgium and Luxembourg. Iron ore output in France is showing a tendency to decline as a result of preference of the European Economic Community steel producers for high grade imported ores. France also imports some ore to meet the needs of the recently established steel plant at Dunkirk.

Spain

The iron ore deposits of economic importance in Spain are located in the northern provinces close to tidewater in the provinces of Lugo, León, Oviedo, Santander, Viscaya, and Avilés. The deposits near Bilbao have been the mainstay of the iron ore industry of Spain but are now of declining importance. The positive and probable reserves of ore in Spain are estimated at 880 million tons. Spain exports iron ore to West Germany, the United Kingdom, and France.

Sweden

The iron deposits of Sweden lie in three geographic regions: Swedish Lapland at Kiruna and Gällivare, central Sweden, and at Taberg, in southern Sweden. The iron ores of Swedish Lapland, the Kiruna ores, form the largest reserve of magnetite in Europe. The best grade of ore contains 68 per cent iron. This ore body was formerly worked by open pit mining but is now being developed by underground methods.

Sweden exports most of its ore output to West Germany, the United Kingdom, and Belgium–Luxembourg. Additional small quantities are shipped to other west European nations. The ore is shipped by rail to the ice-free port of Narvik in northern Norway on the Ofoten Fjord, or through the port of Lulea at the head of the Gulf of Bothnia. Ice closes this port for about six months out of the year. The Swedish producers are meeting with increased competition in the European market from the West African ores.

Germany

Germany produces a modest quantity of ore grading about 27 per cent iron content. The principal deposit is the Salzgitter in the Weser district. A recent deposit at Staffhorst wih iron content of 37 per cent may reverse the downward trend of domestic iron ore output. Germany depends mainly on imported high grade ores for her requirements. The principal sources, other than the low grade ores of the French Lorraine, are Sweden, Brazil and Liberia.

United Kingdom

The iron ore reserves of the United Kingdom, in terms of iron content, are exceeded, in Europe, only by France and Sweden. The grade of ore is about 30 per cent in the existing ore bodies. The ores of the Cleveland district, once the source of high grade ore, have been exhausted. The domestic ore industry is gradually declining, reflecting an increase in the ratio of imported ore to home ore consumed. This is now approximately 2:1, based on the iron content of all ores consumed in the steel making industry. Imports are obtained from a wide variety of sources. The principal import nation is Sweden, followed by Canada, Venezuela, and Liberia. Other suppliers of lesser rank are Brazil, Norway, Spain, Algeria, Sierra Leone, and the Republic of South Africa.

major iron ore reserves of Europe

The relative importance of major iron resources of Europe are indicated in Table 2.1.

TABLE 2.1

Major European Iron Ore Reserves
(Excluding large low-grade deposits)

Country	Quantity 000	Approximate grade % Fe
France	8,000,000	30-55
Germany, West	1,600,000	30
Sweden	3,500,000	58-68
United Kingdom	4,600,000	25-30

the Soviet Union

The proved reserves of economic iron ore in the Soviet Union are placed at 46 billion tons as of January 1, 1962. The reserves of high grade, averaging 56 per cent, iron are no more than 9 billion tons. More than half of the known reserves of ore lie in the European Russian, in the Ukraine, Kursk, and the Kerch Peninsula. About one-third of the known reserves occur in the Ural-Kazakhstan district (Mt. Magnitnaya at Magnitogorsk, and Kustanay to the east). Elsewhere, the U.S.S.R.'s known iron ore resources are meager, especially in the far east. Nonetheless, retarded geological surveys may disclose new discoveries of large or high grade deposits.

The Krivoi Rog ore body, one of the two most important deposits in the Soviet Union, is located in a narrow zone with the town of Krivoi Rog in the center. The field is large but the quality of ore varies. Iron content of some of the main seams is as high as 60 per cent, while the easily mined ores on the edge are as low as 36 per cent. Deposits of excellent coking coal and metallurgical limestone lie within a distance of 200 miles from the Krivoi ores. There are smelting and metallurgical works in the Don Basin, Zhdanov, Taganrog, and Krivoi Rog.

Kerch, situated at the extreme east of the Crimean Peninsula, is also the center point of a large ore body. The ore is low grade, only about 35 per cent iron content, but it lies in thick beds nearer the surface than the Krivoi Rog ores, and it is mined more cheaply. Ores from the Kerch field cover the requirements of the iron and steel works at Kerch and at Zhdanov.

Transcaucasia possesses reserves of iron ore at Dashkesan, some 10 miles south of Kirovabad. The known and possible deposits are as high as 175 million tons of magnetic iron ore of 55 per cent iron content.

Ural-Kazakhstan has become one of the leading iron mining districts in the U.S.S.R. The most important ore mining district is Mt. Magnitnaya. Other deposits are located in the Sverdlovsk region at Orsk, Bakal, Beloretsk, Kura and Molotov. These ore deposits have been made the basis of an iron and steel industry with coking coal supplied by the Karaganda coal field, 800 miles to the east in Kazakh S.S.R. The distribution of iron ore reserve by region or basin, in per cent, is given in Table 2.2.

India

Some of the richest iron ore deposits in the world, many of which have not as yet been surveyed, lie in India. High grade ore reserves are estimated at 21,000 million tons. The largest known deposits are in

TABLE 2.2

Iron Ore Reserves of the U.S.S.R.

Region or basin	Grade of ore % Fe	Reserve
Ural-Kazakhstan	33	32
Kursh Magnetic Anomaly	51	25
Krivoi Rog	44	24
East Siberia	39	9
Kola-Karelia	32	4
Kerch	37	3
West Siberia	39	2
Dashkesan	40	small
Far East	39	1

the states of Bihar and Orissa. Also, large deposits of high grade hematite are located in Madhya Pradesh State. Other deposits are located in Mysore State and in Goa, on the west coast.

The vast extent and location of the ore bodies is favorable to both a domestic and export market. India has currently six iron and steel plants, two privately owned and four in the so-called public sector. Of the two privately owned plants, the Tata Iron and Steel Company, located at Jamshedpur, is the largest. The other privately owned plant is the Iron and Steel Company at Burnpur, about one-half the size of Tata. The government owned plants are located at Durgapur, in Bihar State, Rourkela in Orissa State and Bhilai. Ore in the states of Bihar and Orissa are near to India's most important coal fields. These deposits supply four of India's steel plants. Ore deposits in Madhya Pradesh State supply the steel mill at Bhilai.

India's vast iron ore reserves provide an ample base for export in addition to the domestic market. About 40 per cent of India's iron ore production is exported, of which two-thirds goes to Japan. For this market, the Indian iron ore industry has developed a mine at Bailadila to supply Japan with direct shipping ore and a pellet plant at Goa to supply Japan with a half million tons of pellets annually. Iron from the mine at Bailadila will be shipped through a port at Paradip, in Orissa, which can accommodate bulk ore carriers from 40,000 to 60,000 DWT.

China

Iron ore is widely distributed in mainland China. While details of the incidence of iron ore deposits are not known, the location of iron and steel plants imply concentrations of iron ore in many parts of the country. The expansion of iron ore output in the decade of 1955 to 1964 from a little more than 7 million tons to a reported 36 million tons in 1964 indicates the rate of development in the iron and steel industry. The iron and steel industry of mainland China is concentrated in eight major centers of which the most important is Anshan in Manchuria. Second in importance is the steel plant at Wuhan. Other plants of importance are Paotois, Shihchingshan, Tientsen, Shanghai, Taiyuan, and Chungking.

The Ores of Africa

The African continent is emerging as one of the important iron ore producing continents of the world. In the decade from 1955 to 1964, output rose from 10 million tons to 30 million tons and a rapid expansion in the immediate future is indicated. Northern Africa has long contributed to the ore needs of European nations and, in recent years, western African producers are assuming a leading role in this market. The United States, also, has become a customer. Producers on the Mediterranean coast of Africa are Algeria, Tunisia and Morocco. The United Arab Republic began production in a small way in 1956. The ores of North Africa are about 54 per cent iron, less than the West African ores, and as a result are gradually losing out in the European market. Output is showing signs of a downward trend.

In West Africa, ore deposits of varying degrees of grade and quality occur in Mauritania, Upper Volta, Ghana, Guinea, Liberia, Sierra Leone, Cameroon, Gabon, and Angola. The three producers of importance are Liberia, Mauritania, and Sierra Leone. These three account for 90 per cent of West Africa's production.

In Liberia, iron ore is mined in the Bomi Hills, above Monrovia, in the Bong and Nimba Mountains. The earliest producer (1951) is the Liberia Mining Company with a mine in the Bomi Hills with rail connections to the port of Monrovia. The ore is destined mainly for the United States. The more recent, and larger, development is the Lamco concession in the Nimba Mountains on the Guinea border. The Lamco project is a joint venture formed to exploit the 250 million ton deposit of high grade hematite ores with an iron content of 65 per cent. The entire project includes the construction of a new ocean port at Buchanan and a 170-mile railway from mine to port. Vessels of 65,000 DWT will be accommodated. An ore washing and pelletizing plant has also been built at Buchanan. This represents the largest industrial project completed in Africa to date (1963). The ore is shipped to France, West Germany, Italy, the Netherlands, and the United Kingdom.

A third producer, the Bong Mining Company, mines and concentrates low grade ore in the Bong Hills for shipment mainly to Germany.

In 1963, an extensive deposit of high grade iron ore near Fort Gourand, in Mauritania, was opened to production, with shipments to European nations. The deposits, near the Mauritania-Spanish Sahara border, have an iron content of 64 per cent. The reserves are placed at 125 million tons proven ore with an additional 75 million as probable ore.

Sierra Leone produces and exports somewhat less than 2 million tons annually, mainly to West Germany and the United Kingdom.

In southern Africa, two developments are of interest. The Republic of South Africa has a small iron ore industry, the output of which is used mainly in a domestic iron and steel industry. Limited supplies of coking coal are available in the extensive coal deposits of South Africa.

In Swaziland, a deposit of high grade hematite is being mined and shipped to Japan through the port of Lourenço Marques. The harbor can accommodate 77,500 DWT vessels, three of which will be used in shipping the ore. Ore reserves are estimated at 30 million tons of direct shipping grade.

Australia

The discovery of vast tonnages of iron ore in northwestern Australia opens up a new era in the mining industry of this continent. While the presence of iron ore bodies of considerable size was known as far back as 1888, the magnitude of these deposits was not recognized until about 1960. The iron bearing districts are grouped in a broad belt or zone from Cockatoo Island and Yampi Sound, to Mount Whaleback, inland from King Sound. From north to south, the major iron provinces are the Kimberley Basin, the Pilbara, and the Hamersley Iron Province. The most important mine in the Kimberley Basin is the mine on Cockatoo and Koolan islands. In the Pilbara district, Mount Goldsworthy is the most prominent deposit. The proved reserves of 30 million tons are 65 per cent iron in the form of hematite. There is an added equivalent of 59 to 64 per cent hematite.

The Hamersley Iron Province is economically the most important of the western Australia iron ore deposits. It is reported to contain 14 billion of the 15 billion tons of western Australian iron ore. The area embraces the Hamersley and Opthalmia ranges. Minor iron ore deposits occur in western and southwestern Australia.

Iron output in Australia in a decade rose from a modest 2 million tons in 1950 to 8 million tons in 1966.

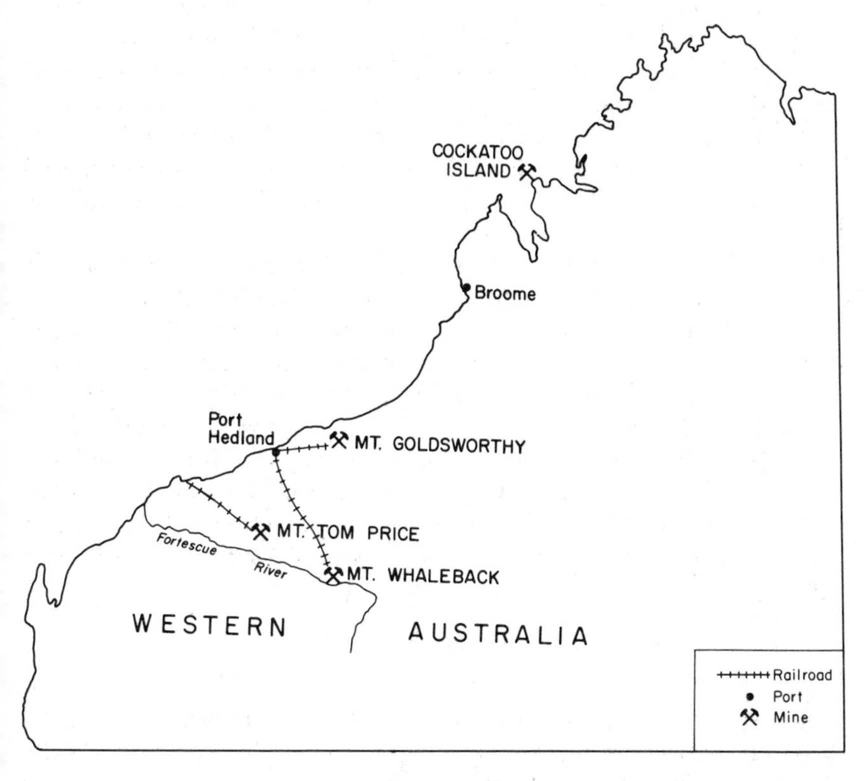

FIGURE 2.3 Iron Ore Developments in Australia

The Australian iron industry is irrevocably linked with the demands of the steel industry in Japan. It is about 3000 miles from Port Hedland or Dampier to Osaka. The initial market will be entirely Japanese, but with increasing demand world wide markets in Europe may also emerge. The key to the low cost shipment of Australian iron ores is an efficient transportation system in all of its units: rail, port facilities, ocean vessels. Three railroad lines are built or are being constructed from Mount Tom Price to Dampier, 179 miles to King Sound, from Mount Whaleback, and another line from Mount Goldsworthy to Port Hedland, a distance of 70 miles. Railroads are all standard gauge and built to carry 100 long-ton ore cars. On the Hamersley Range, the largest of Australia's iron ore developments, the railroad has been designed and built to transport 40 million tons of ore per year.

Dormant or Inactive Iron Ore Bodies

There are, in addition to the iron ore deposits that are being currently mined, a number of ore bodies that are not being exploited. Among these are Baja California, Guerrero and Oaxaca in Mexico, Tambo Grande in Peru, El Loco in Chile, Sierra Grande in Argentina, South of Niamey in Upper Volta, Shiene in Ghana, Chaines des Mameblec in Cameroon, Mekambo area in Gabon, Postmasburg in the Republic of South Africa, and Madras in India.

Chapter 3

Iron-Making Fuels and Alloys

The Ferroalloys

An alloy steel is a grade of steel in which one or more alloying elements have been blended to give it special properties that cannot be obtained in carbon steel. Generally speaking, it is advisable to use alloy steel when more strength, ductility, and toughness are required than can be obtained in carbon steel. Alloy grade should also be used where specific properties such as corrosion-resistance, heat-resistance, and special low-temperature impact values are needed.

In terms of productiveness, machines or tools made of alloy steels can do more work, run faster with safety, bear heavier loads, withstand higher pressures and temperatures, resist attacks from acids or alkalis, or in other ways behave as superior tools for the tasks of industry. The steel alloy as an industrial material has become indispensable to modern industrial production. Nature did not arrange the deposits of ferroalloy materials to be convenient to the steel-producing districts of the world. With the possible exception of the Soviet Union, no nation has a complete array of iron alloys to insure self-sufficiency. The industrial nations of the Atlantic Basin, in Europe and North America, must obtain their essential alloying materials from deposits located in foreign territory.

manganese

Manganese is one of the most basic and essential elements in alloy and carbon steels. It far exceeds in output all the other ferroalloys combined. The mineral is produced in 40 countries but six countries, each producing more than a million tons, account for 80 per cent of the output. These are the U.S.S.R., India, Brazil, Republic of South Africa, mainland China, and Gabon. Countries that produce less than a million tons but more than 100,000 tons include Ghana, Republic of the Congo, Morocco, Japan, Rumania, Mexico, Ivory Coast, Hungary and Guyana. Altogether these 15 nations account for 96 per cent of the output.

The U.S.S.R. leads the world in manganese output. The principal developed deposits are at Nikopol, in southeastern U.S.S.R., north of the Caucasus, and the Chiatura deposit in the Georgian S.S.R. The latter deposit may be classed as the largest single deposit known; estimates of the total commercial ore range from 44 to 200 million tons. Because of quality, quantity, accessibility, and low cost mining, the Chiatura deposit has been a dominant factor in the world manganese market. The principal foreign markets are Poland, East Germany, Czechoslovakia, France, the United Kingdom, Japan and Germany.

India's chief deposits of manganese are in the Central Provinces, Bombay, Orissa, Madras, Mysore, and Goa. Orissa is the largest producing state. Other important producing states are Mysore, Madhya Pradesh and Maharashtra. Reserves of all classes of manganese in India were estimated at 60 million tons of marketable ore. The principal foreign markets are in Japan, the United States, West Germany, the United Kingdom and Czechoslovakia.

In Brazil, manganese, next to iron ore, is the most important mineral export. Reserves of known deposits may total from 100 to 150 million tons. About two-thirds occur in the deposits in Urucum district of Mato Grosso and most of the remainder is in deposits in the Territory of Amapá and in the states of Minas Gerais and Bahía. Principal production is in Amapá. Most of the output in Amapá is sold to the United States.

Mainland China's output of manganese is reported to be of low grade.

In the Republic of South Africa, ore reserves of manganese are reported to be very large, but estimates of tonnages are unavailable. There are two widely separated manganese fields. The most important is the Postmasburg, discovered in 1922. The other manganese area is in Transvall Province. Durban is the chief port of export.

Among the six large producers of the world, Gabon has among the largest known reserves, estimated at 200 million tons of ore. Output began in 1962 and rapidly rose to more than 1 million tons. It is the most valuable production of the nation. The ore body consists of beds 4 to 6 meters thick with a thin overburden. The opening of this deposit and its rapid expansion has introduced a new competitive factor in the manganese industry. The principal importers are the United States, France, West Germany, Japan, Spain and Italy.

chromium

The uses of chromium steels are many and varied. Among more familiar items that often contain chromium are hand tools, gears, springs, turbine wheels, ball and roller bearings, and shafts. Chromium steels are relatively stable at high temperatures and are often used where resistance to heat is important.

The five leading producers of chromite ores are the U.S.S.R., Republic of South Africa, Philippines, Rhodesia, and Turkey. These produce more than 80 per cent of world output.

The ultimate reserve of chromium in South Africa is considered by many chromite authorities to be the largest in the world. The present minable reserve is reported to be about 200 million tons. Most of the ore is exported to the United States; minor quantities are shipped to West Germany, the United Kingdom, and the Netherlands.

Rhodesia is among the five large producers of chromite. The United States is the principal importer of Rhodesian chromite, followed by Western European nations. The Philippines ranks third in world production of chromite. The ore is exported almost entirely to the United States, the United Kingdom, and Japan. Turkey is fifth among the world producers. The ore is destined for the United States, the nations of Western Europe and Japan.

molybdenum

Molybdenum ore is produced in 11 nations, but the United States accounts for two-thirds of world output. The U.S.S.R., Chile and China produce moderate amounts. Canada is expected to increase output substantially in the immediate future.

nickel

There are three important nickel producing areas in the world: Canada, the U.S.S.R. and New Caledonia. These three account for 90 per cent of the output. More than 50 per cent comes from Canada alone. Small contributions come from 12 other nations.

Nickel is used primarily as an alloying material and most of it is used as an alloy of steel. Steels containing nickel have high tensile strength, great elasticity, superior hardness, and resistance to wear and shock. Monel metal, an alloy of nickel, copper, and iron is highly resistant to salt water.

The largest of the Canadian nickel mines is located in the Sudbury district, north of Lake Ontario. A small development and mine is lo-

located at Lynn Lake, Manitoba. In addition to these, there are small mines in Ontario, northwestern Quebec, and near Hope, British Columbia.

tungsten

Manufacturing industries are able to turn out large quantities of goods because the machine tools used in making machines are so fast and so efficient. In the machine tool, the metal tungsten is pivotal. Machine tools made of tungsten steel permit a higher output per man and machine than is possible with carbon-steel tools. The main characteristic of high-speed tungston-steel tools is that they maintain a sharp cutting edge at working temperatures far above those that ruin carbon-steel tools. Tungsten carbide is an important material in the production of metal cutting tools, high-velocity armor-piercing projectiles, and equipment for rock drilling. The geographical distribution of tungsten ores gives this metal high strategic importance. China, the U.S.S.R., North Korea, and South Korea produce 70 per cent of the world total. The United States is fourth, but produces only 14 per cent. Bolivia, Portugal, and Australia each supply about 3 per cent.

vanadium

In the United States vanadium is obtained principally from uranium-vanadium ores in New Mexico, Colorado, Utah, and Arizona. Vanadium is also produced in the Republic of South Africa and southwest Africa.

Reductants

Up to now we have discussed iron ore, the raw material of a productive economy. We are now concerned with the key that will open the way for the manufacture of iron-made goods. We must concern ourselves with reducing agents.

A reducing agent acts to free the metal from the ore in which it is contained in its natural state. This, in the case of iron ore, means separating the metal from the oxygen to which it is bound in the ore. There are only two reducing agents that are feasible for ore reduction: carbon as carbon monoxide, and hydrogen. The use of the latter is technically possible but economically not feasible.

The primary and very fundamental step of freeing the metal iron from its ore has two requirements: carbon in some form to unite with the oxygen in the ore and set the metal free, and heat to bring the temperature in the blast furnace up to the point where the freeing of the metal takes place. This two-fold necessity is emphasized far too infrequently. One hears expressions of smelting iron ore by means of electric power, usually hydro, as if electricity alone can accomplish ore reduction. Electricity can supply heat for the operation; it does not act as a reductant.

The role of a reducing agent in the iron and steel industry, the source of the reductant, and geographical distribution have an important bearing on the geographical pattern of iron and steel manufacture. The quantity of a reductant needed to produce a ton of free iron is large. Ore and reducing coal either must be closely associated geographically, or one must move to the location of the other. In the present day pattern of ore production, the close association of coking coal and iron ore is the exception rather than the rule, and transportation of one or both is unavoidable. Also, in the wide search for ores in all continents, ocean movements of steel-making materials are equally unavoidable. There remains then to examine the conditions under which the essential materials are assembled. Which is most advantageous, to move ore to coking coal locations or vice versa? There is no clear-cut rule. How does this affect the location of steel plants?

In this analysis of the role of reducing agents, we are concerned primarily with the effect, if any, of the deep-sea transportation of steel-making materials. Does the role of coke, the reductant of the iron and steel industry, bring about an increasing ocean movement of iron ore to entrenched steel centers? Or does it, in conjunction with low-cost transportation, bring about a dispersion of the steel industry beyond the pre-war bounds? Or do both of these conditions appear?

We can attempt to evaluate the role of iron reductants only if we examine the characteristics of the material; the physical and economic role that it plays in primary iron and steel production.

In blast furnace operation, carbon is usually supplied in the form of coke, a product derived from the distillation of coal. It is the fuel used in iron reduction. Carbon is also supplied in such supplementary fuels as natural gas, fuel oil, or possibly powdered coal. In actually reducing iron ore, coke is oxydized to gaseous carbon monoxide, in which form it reacts with iron ore to remove the oxygen and set the metal free.

fuels for iron reduction

The fundamental fact that must be grasped in considering iron supply for industry is that iron is as much a product of fuel as it is of the metal-bearing ore itself. Moreover, it is equally essential to understand that in the process of manufacturing—from ore to finished automobile, corn planter, or Boy Scout knife—the fuel that is needed to get over the first step of converting the ore to the pig-iron and steel-ingot stage seems like an inordinately large part of the total fuels needed in manufacture; about 33 per cent. It takes almost one ton of coking coal to supply the coke to smelt one ton of pig iron. Moreover, the fuel that can be used in the large-scale blast furnace for the production of iron on a large scale must be a hard, porous, strong load-bearing coke which is made from coal.

Nor have we as yet included all the necessary factors. This coke must be low in sulfur, to keep the percentage of the harmful material to a very small percentage in the resultant pig iron. While all other steps in manufacturing can, with occasional exceptions, use oil and gas as well as coal for the needed fuel requirements, the initial step in the manufacturing process—getting the metal out of the ore—can be taken, for all practical purposes, only with coke from coal. This fuel is so special and exacting in its nature that a special term, "coking coal," is applied to those coals from which coke or (more narrowly) metallurgical coke can be made.

To supply the blast furnace with suitable fuel, a special fuel processing industry, the manufacture of coke, must be set up. This involves considerable investment and processing cost, which is reflected in a high unit cost of fuel used in the reduction of iron ore. Investment in a coke oven and blast furnace plant runs to about 80 million dollars.

what an aspiring nation must obtain

The high financial and exacting physical requirements of the blast furnace point out, in unmistakable terms, the problems that an industrially undeveloped nation encounters in aspiring to enter the community of industrial nations. We might point out that a nation like Brazil, endowed with ample quantities of the world's finest iron ore must import a ton of coal for each ton of free iron metal she wishes to produce. If, for instance, we were to visualize the transformation of her 80 million + people into an industrial nation comparable in output to Western Europe (an output of about 500 pounds of iron per person), she would need to produce 20 million tons of metal and obtain an equivalent quantity of coking coal of which she has none. Imports of coal at $20 to $25 a ton, would call for an outlay of half a billion dollars, a not inconsiderable sum in the Brazilian economy. More will be said of this subsequently. First, it is necessary to examine the world situation.

what the coking coal supply situation is

Against the background of coking coal needs and coking coal supplies in the ocean-based iron and steel industry of the world, coking coal is in short supply. Among the nations of the Atlantic Basin and in Japan and India, the geographical distribution of coking coal is severely restricted. Japan is without a domestic supply; South American nations have practically none; Africa is limited to coal of South Africa and Rhodesia (and that in limited quantities). Coking coal supplies in northwestern Europe are sizable but inadequate for this area's industrial base; Italy depends entirely upon imported supplies. India's problem is one of finding enough coking coal for their planned iron and steel industry; Canada and Mexico have meager quantities. Today, *only* the United States, among the group of free nations, has a supply of coking coal ample for a large industry at home and an exportable surplus for nations deficient in supply.

While United States reserves are large, by comparison with Europe, and cost of production is low, this country is approaching the time when the thick seams (42 inches or more) can no longer meet the needs of the coke-oven industry. Exploration of thinner seams down to possibly 28 inches in thickness will be necessary with attendant higher costs of production.[1]

In Western Europe the prospects for adequate coking coal production from domestic sources appear unfavorable. Geological, technical, and economic limitations preclude flexibility in coal production to meet the demands for increased output. The greater proportion of coal produced in Western Europe is from seams generally three to four feet in thickness, many of which are steeply inclined at depths from 1000 to 4000 feet below the surface, compared to an average seam thickness of about five feet at an average depth less than 200 feet.[2]

how coking coal is distributed

We are concerned here not with total quantity of coking coal that is produced, but with what is shipped overseas from the United States. The nations of the European Coal and Steel Community do produce a large proportion of their coking coal needs themselves; the contribution from the United States is supplementary. South America is almost entirely dependent on imports, mostly from the United States. Japan gets

[1]Risser, H. E., "Emerging Patterns on Coking Coal Supply," Illinois Geol. Survey, Series 10-S, July, 1958.

[2]Rice, G. S., and Irving Hartman, "Coal Mining in Europe," Bulletin 414, U.S. Bureau of Mines, 1939.

coal for coking purposes from several nations, but depends upon the United States to supply the quality coal with which coal from other sources is blended to make a metallurgical coke. In substance, for Europe, Latin America, Canada and Japan, the United States supplies that added quantity of coke that sustains the pig iron output and the ensuing industrial output at its existing high level. Table 3.1 shows what happened from 1954 to 1967 in coal exports from the United States to diverse areas.

TABLE 3.1

Coal Exports from the U.S. to Diverse Areas

To	1954-63 Average	1967
ECSC	20,697	16,241
Other Europe	5,074	3,072
Canada	14,482	15,374
Other North America	76	73
South America	1,893	2,562
Japan	4,580	12,720
Africa	120	6

Coal destined to ECSC countries is predominately for coke manufacture. This is also the case for Japan and South American nations. A portion of Canadian imports are also used for coke manufacture, but steam coal and domestic fuel also loom large.

Chapter **4**

Solid Fuels

Each year the world uses nearly 5 billion tons of energy as coal equivalent. Fuel and power resources come mainly from four natural sources: coal, petroleum, natural gas, and water power. Oil shale shows promise of becoming an economic source of liquid fuel. The tar sands of Alberta, Canada, are also being exploited to a limited degree. The use of nuclear energy as a source of power is now established and, although the present contribution to the supply of electric power is small, a substantial increase is expected.

The raw fuels, as mined from the earth or pumped from wells, are not very useful to industry; most of them have to be specially prepared to perform the tasks of industry. We need several types of solid, liquid, and gaseous fuels. We also need electric power, which is energy in non-material form.

The industrial economy of the United States was founded upon coal. The more recent use of petroleum and natural gas has added versatility to the kinds of productive activities that can make use of power. Because of this wide variety and excellent geographic distribution of fuels it has been possible to carry out processes and to apply power to productive activities which would not be possible if we had access to only one fuel.

Coal

The known and estimated coal reserves of the world lie almost entirely in the lands of the Northern Hemisphere. The outstanding coal resource nations are the United States, the U.S.S.R., China and Germany. The estimated reserves, in detail, are presented in Table 4.1.

TABLE 4.1

Estimated Remaining Coal Reserves of the World by Region and Principal Coal-Producing Countries

Region and Country	Producible Coal (x 10^9 metric tons)	Per cent of Regional Total	Per cent of World Total
Asia:			
U.S.S.R.	600	52.3	25.8
China	506	44.1	21.8
India	32	2.8	1.4
Japan	5	0.4	0.2
Others	4	0.4	0.2
Total	1,147	100.0	49.4
North America:			
United States	753	94.4	32.5
Canada	43	5.4	1.8
Mexico	2	0.2	0.1
Total	798	100.0	34.4
Europe:			
Germany	143	47.5	6.2
United Kingdom	85	28.2	3.7
Poland	40	13.3	1.7
Czechoslovakia	10	3.3	0.4
France	6	2.0	0.3
Belgium	3	1.0	0.1
Netherlands	2	0.7	0.1
Others	12	4.0	0.5
Total	301	100.0	13.0
Africa:			
Union of South Africa	34	97.1	1.5
Others	1	2.9	-
Total	35	100.0	1.5
Australasia:			
Australia	29	99.0	1.3
Others	-	1.0	-
Total	29	100.0	1.3
South and Central America:			
Colombia	6	60.0	0.2
Venezuela	2	20.0	0.1
Others	2	20.0	0.1
Total	10	100.0	0.4
WORLD TOTAL	2,320		100.0

[1] From: Averitt, Paul, 1961, "Coal Reserves of the United States and of the World," p. 5 in Domestic and World Resources of Fossil Fuels, Radioactive Minerals, and Geothermal Energy; Preliminary Reports Prepared by Members of the U. S. Geological Survey for the Natural Resources Subcommittee of the Federal Science Council.

World coal production is reflected in the relative abundance of supply in each nation and area. The older industrial nations such as the United Kingdom and the ECSC together are producing out of proportion to their reserves, but are showing a tendency to decline in output.

Coal Fields of the United States and Canada

The United States has widely distributed coal deposits, but they are unequally distributed according to rank. Only 30 per cent of our total coal reserves are east of the Mississippi River, yet this area contains 60 per cent of our reserves of bituminous coal and anthracite. The coals west of the river consist mostly of lignite and sub-bituminous coal. For purposes of economic analysis the coal resources of the United States are classified into six provinces: Eastern Coal Province, Eastern Interior, Western Interior, Gulf, Great Plains, Rocky Mountain and Pacific. The commercially important provinces are the Eastern (Appalachian) and the Eastern Interior. Together they produce 95 per cent of the nation's coal output. The Appalachian field alone produces more than 70 per cent.

the eastern (Appalachian) coal province

The Eastern Coal Province ranks as the greatest storehouse of high-rank coal in the United States. The product of this field plays an important role in both the domestic and the foreign market. In the domestic market it is the principal source of coal for the manufacture of metallurgical coke. Coal for this market originates in western Pennsylvania, southern West Virginia, and eastern Kentucky, and moves by all-rail haul to the steel centers in Sparrows Point, Lackawanna, and eastern Ohio, and to Pittsburgh by barge. Coking coal for the Illinois-Indiana steel district, centering around Chicago, is shipped by rail to Lake Erie ports and thence by lake colliers to ports on Lake Michigan.

Coal from Virginia, West Virginia, and eastern Kentucky moves to tidewater ports at Hampton Roads, New York and Philadelphia, and then to the New England market and other coastwise destinations. The largest single outlet is the electric utility market.

Coal mined in Alabama finds its principal market locally in coke manufacture for the iron and steel industry and electric utilities.

Foreign Markets

The Appalachian coal field plays a significant role in the foreign market. The principal markets are Canada, European Coal and Steel

Community, and Japan. The Canadian market is one of long standing and averages about 14 million tons annually. The markets in Europe and Japan have developed since World War II. In Western Europe the severe coal shortage immediately following the end of the war has been overcome, but there is a continuing deficit of coal for the production of metallurgical coke. Local supplies of coking coal are available in West Germany, France and Belgium, but in insufficient quantities for the needs of the steel industry. These shortages are prevalent in all nations comprising the European Coal and Steel Community. Italy, a nation devoid of coal supplies, depends almost entirely upon the United States for metallurgical coal supplies and will continue to do so indefinitely.

The United States ships in excess of 5 million tons of metallurgical grade coal annually to Japan as fuel for the expanding Japanese coal industry. This is a postwar development directly related to Japan's growing steel industry. High rank, metallurgical coal from the United States is needed to blend with Japan's other major source of coal, Australia, in order to make a satisfactory blast furnace fuel. Until coal suitable for coking is found in Australia, or sources of fuel are obtained from the Asiatic mainland, coal from the Appalachian field will remain an important mainstay to the Japanese steel industry.

Other minor outlets for coal are South and Central America.

the eastern interior coal field

This field comprises coal deposits in Illinois, Indiana, and western Kentucky. The minable coal seams are generally thick and lie horizontally, adaptable for machine mining. In Illinois 60 per cent of the proven coal deposits are more than six feet thick. These Eastern Interior fields are unusually well adapted for mechanized production. Output per man, per day, in Illinois and Indiana is 27 tons against a national average of 17 tons. The principal markets are the electric utility plants in the Chicago and St. Louis areas, with minor outlets in industry and retail trade.

western coal

The vast reserve of coal west of the Mississippi River in no less than 13 states is unimportant in the energy market today. The largest tonnage is lignite and most of the remainder is coal of sub-bituminous rank. Limited deposits of coking coal at Helper, Utah, and Raton Mesa, New Mexico, supply metallurgical fuel for blast furnaces at Pueblo,

Colorado, Geneva, Utah, and Fontana, California. Altogether the western states account for about 5 per cent of the nation's output.

Canada

Canada has large coal deposits, chiefly in the Great Plains region, but also minor quantities in Nova Scotia on the east, and on Vancouver Island and in British Columbia on the west. The lignite and sub-bituminous coal fields of the Canadian prairie provinces are continuations of similar coal fields in the United States, and the deposits are extensive.

The problems facing the Canadian coal industry are not due to lack of reserves, but are associated with the geographic relationships of the mines to the centers of consumption. The most highly industrialized sections of Canada are located in the south-central part of Ontario and southwestern Quebec. The cities of Toronto and Montreal are in the heart of the areas described. The distance from the bituminous coal fields in Alberta and British Columbia is about 2000 miles to Toronto and 2275 miles to Montreal. From the Maritime Province mines it is 1350 miles to Toronto and 1020 miles to Montreal.

The Value of Coal

The economic value of a coal bed or deposit is governed by its geographical location with respect to coal markets and by the physical, chemical, and thermal characteristics of the coal itself.

A classification of coal has been established to differentiate empirically the characteristics of heat (BTU) content, moisture content, and volatile content. In the market place coal is also graded according to the content of mineral matter; sulfur or other deleterious material.

The depth of a coal seam and its thickness also have a bearing on the economic value of a coal deposit. About 25 per cent of the measured and indicated coal reserves in beds 28 inches or more in thickness are less than 2000 feet below the surface. The remaining 75 per cent is inferred reserves, reserves in thin beds, and reserves 2000 to 3000 feet below the surface.

Thickness of seam has a direct bearing on the output of coal per man-day, the degree of possible mechanization of mining, and the resultant cost of recovering the coal. Thickness of coal seams are empirically classified into three categories: more than 42 inches; 28 to 42 inches; and 14 to 28 inches.

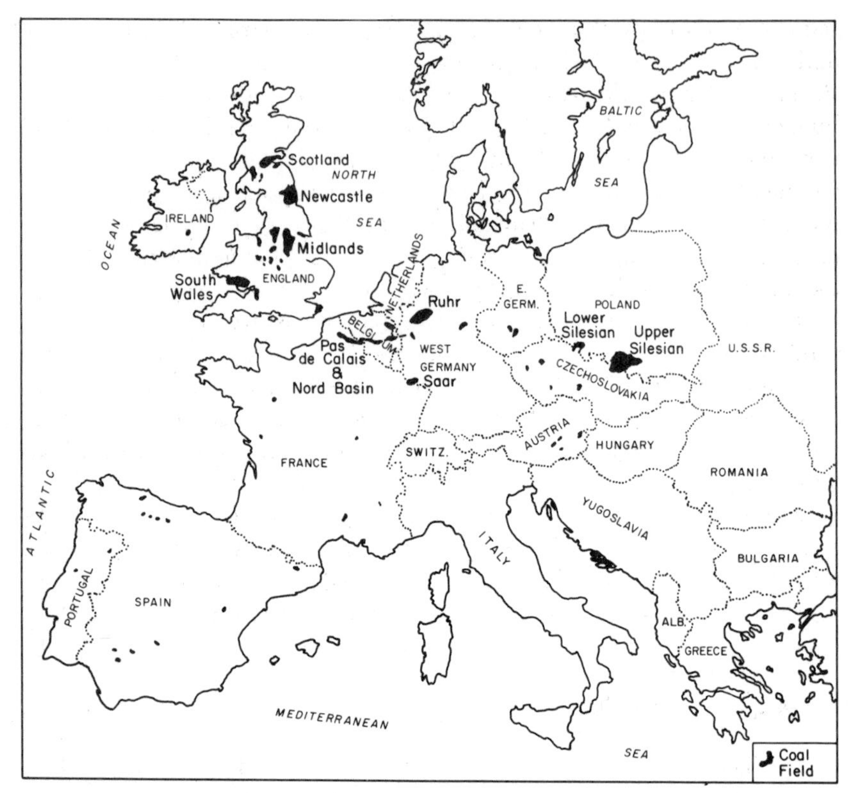

FIGURE 4.1 Principal Coal Fields of Europe

Coal in Europe

The major coal fields of Europe are shown on Figure 4.1. The principal coal fields and their locations are, in the United Kingdom, the Southwestern, Midlands, Yorkshire, Scottish, and Northumberland and Durham coal basins; in West Germany, the Ruhr, Saar, Aachen, and the brown coal deposits in the Rhineland; in France, the Pas-de-Calais, Nord, and Lorraine; in Belgium, the deposits of Campine, Liege, Charleroi, Centre, and Borinage. In Eastern Europe are the large reserves of brown coal in East Germany, the large reserves of bituminous coal in Poland, and deposits of hard coal and brown coal in Czechoslovakia. Other minor deposits are scattered through several European nations.

coal in the United Kingdom

The coal industry of the United Kingdom served two functions during the period of British industrial supremacy: it provided coal for industrial purposes at home, and it supplied a surplus for bunker fuel and for export to the nations that supplied raw materials to Great Britain. After World War II, the British coal industry declined, the bunker market was lost to fuel oil, and the export market suffered both from competition with oil and with expanded coal production on the continent. Moreover, coal reserves near the surface and much at medium depth had been exhausted. Under these adverse economic conditions, the coal mines were nationalized in 1947 and the operation of the mines became a function of the *National Coal Board.* When the NCB took over the British industry, the mines were in a run-down condition due to lack of maintenance and repair. Also, mining methods were almost primitive. Under a program of modernization and consolidation, and closing of high cost mines, the coal industry has been restored to economic health and is now producing about 200 million tons yearly.

Britain's major source of fuel for all purposes is coal, but in decreasing proportions. From 87 per cent of all fuels in 1954, the percentage fell to less than 70 per cent in 1965. The advent of gas from North Sea fields will reduce this percentage still further.

Western Europe

For nearly 100 years the basis of the industrial development of Western Europe, in Germany, northern France, Belgium, Luxembourg, and the Netherlands, has been coal.

> By drawing a line on the map of western Europe, beginning at Calais in France, southeastward to Strasbourg on the Rhine near the French-German border, thence almost due north to Hamm in the Land North-Rhine-Westphalia in Germany and, finally, due west to the starting point at Calais, the area enclosed would represent this "triangle." Within it lies the major coal fields of western Europe. In Germany are the Ruhr, Aachen and the Saar deposits of hard coal and the lignite, or brown coal, of the Cologne area. In the Netherlands, the mines of the Limbourg field are close by the deposits of the Campine, Liege, Charleroi, Centre and the Borinage of Belgium, which are, in turn, contiguous to those of the Pas-de-Calais and Nord fields of France. Adjacent to the Saar mines of Germany are those of the French field of Lorraine. Not only is this area blessed with extensive deposits of coal; it is also fortunate in having the Rhine, Meuse, Schelde and the Moselle rivers as means of transportation. Given the natural waterways, inter-connected by a well-developed system of canals and supplemented by an integrated railway and highway network, the problems of transporting the heavy raw materials or the more refined finished products to either internal markets or to the seaports for overseas exports, are easily solved.

> With all its natural advantages, this area also has its disadvantages. The coal, although plentiful, lies deep in the earth and, in many instances, in seams that are either pitched or deformed, or both. Despite remarkable advances in mining techniques, these natural geological conditions make it difficult and expensive to bring the coal out of the ground. Furthermore, within the past decade the appearance of oil and natural gas on the energy markets of western Europe has created a competitive situation which has caused considerable concern to the producers and consumers of coal. This in turn, has created political, social and economic problems which are not easy to resolve.[1]

By far the most important deposits in the European Community are those of the Ruhr. The excellent coking qualities of Ruhr coal were mainly instrumental in establishing the iron and steel industry in the Ruhr Valley. Moreover, this district also supplied coal and coke for the blast furnaces of the Saar, France, Belgium–Luxembourg, and the Netherlands. Since the close of World War II, the Ruhr coal industry has shared the market with imported coal, mainly from the United States. The cost of coal mined in the Ruhr is high. Although the surface of the Ruhr coal is relatively flat, the coal measures themselves are quite the opposite, being steeply pitched and badly faulted. The combination of increasing depth of mining levels and badly faulted, pitched seams accounts for the relatively high cost per ton for coal recovery in the Ruhr mines.

The second largest coal field in West Germany is located in the Saar. With the development of the use of coal in iron making, the coal of the Saar and the Lorraine iron ores laid the basis of an iron industry in the Saar. This district exports a considerable quantity of coal to France and the low countries, but must import coals of coking quality from the Ruhr and the United States.

The Aachen coal fields near the Dutch border, although small, are significant to Western Europe because they produce a large amount of anthracite and semi-anthracite which is much in demand for domestic fuel.

Brown coal plays an important part in the economy of West Germany. The most important field is in the Rhineland in the area to the west of Cologne. German brown coal has two principal uses: as a source of heat for thermal electric generating plants, and as a raw material for making briquettes.

Coal production in France, Belgium and the Netherlands together adds up to less than 100 million tons. The output is inadequate for the coal requirements of these nations. All of them supplement their do-

---

[1]U.S. Bureau of Mines, *International Coal Trade,* vol. 33, no. 9, pp. 11, 12, Sept. 1964.

mestic output by imports from the United States, West Germany and the United Kingdom. Costs of production in Belgium are high and marginal producers among the mines are gradually being closed.

Coal production in the Netherlands is, in a large measure, of excellent coking quality. The principal output is from state-owned mines.

Poland

Coal mining occupies a leading role in the development of the national economy. Poland is sixth in the world in quantity of coal mined and second to West Germany on the continent. In extent of coal reserves, Poland also ranks second to West Germany and is far ahead of all other continental European nations exclusive of the U.S.S.R.

Polish coal owes its importance to the fact that it has become the basis of the iron and steel industry, electric power, chemical industries and heavy machinery production. By European standards, the production of coal in Poland is efficient. The coal seams are thick and nearly horizontal, and lend themselves favorably to low-cost mining. The productivity of underground mining is 2.10 metric tons per man-shift.

A second factor in the importance of Polish coal is the export trade. This market, particularly in the early period of economic development, provided the nation with the foreign exchange essential to capital formation and investment in industry. Coal is exported mainly to the U.S.S.R., East Germany, Czechoslovakia, Yugoslavia and Hungary, as well as to sixteen nations of Western Europe.

The development, in recent years, of the Rybnik coal basin has added an estimated 6 to 7 billion tons of coal of metallurgical grade to Poland's known coal reserve. Prior to the exploitation and expansion of the Rybnik coal basin, Poland lacked sufficient resources of high quality coking coal to meet its own requirements. With the development of this coal deposit, Poland will be in a position to not only provide for domestic requirements of coking coal but also maintain a sizable export trade. Modern transshipping facilities have been constructed at the port of Szczecin.

brown coal (lignite) in Europe

The significant brown coal producers in Europe are East and West Germany, Czechoslovakia, Yugoslavia, Hungary and Poland. The German states account for two-thirds of Europe's output. In West Germany 95 per cent of the reserves are located in the Rhineland. Brown coal is produced in large open-pit operations using bucket-wheel excavators.

The brown coal is used for power generation and briquetting. In East Germany brown coal is the most important source of energy supply. As in West Germany, brown coal is used for power production, usually near the mine, and in briquet manufacture. The German brown coal has a heating value of about 2/9 of an equivalent weight of bituminous coal.

Coal in Latin America

Coal production and coal resources in Latin America are of small significance in terms of world coal industry. Total output barely exceeds 10 million short tons. There are seven producing nations. Colombian coal reserves are the most extensive of all Latin American countries. On the basis of incomplete surveys, these have been placed at 12 to 20 billion metric tons. The principal deposits are in the Departments of Cundinamarca and Boyaca.

In Brazil, proven reserves in areas under exploitation amount to 1730 million metric tons. The deposits now being mined are in the states of Paraná, Santa Catarina and Rio Grande do Sul. The reserves of Santa Catarina are the most significant, primarily because they contain a fraction of the product suitable for the production of coke after blending with imported coal. Most Brazilian coals are of low standard compared with those of the United States and most European countries.

The coal reserves of Chile are estimated at 735 million metric tons. None of Chile's coals are of metallurgical coking grade but can be used for coke manufacture if blended with imported high quality coking coal.

Peru has numerous coal deposits not yet explored to any great extent. Coal is used by the Cerro Corporation in its mining activities.

Argentina's most important coal reserves are located at Rio Turbio, in southwestern Santa Cruz, and are estimated at 370 million metric tons of low calorie, high-ash coal. Other coal deposits, mainly at the foot of the Andes, are of small importance.

In Mexico, coal reserves are estimated at 2.6 billion tons. The most important coal deposits, both in extent of reserves and quality, are located in the state of Coahuila. Coal is used mainly for the production of coke in the Monclova and Nueva Rosita coke plants.

Coal in the U.S.S.R.

The U.S.S.R. stands second to the United States in the thermal value of coal and lignite produced. Recent data on reserves place the total at 179.0 billion metric tons.[2] By conservative reckoning, the Soviet Union has ample reserves for a long period. The main problem of coal utilization arises from the location of the deposits, the quality of the reserves, especially the limited quantity of coking coals, and in some cases, adverse mining conditions.

The coal industry of the U.S.S.R. is centered in the European section as are most of the large coal using industries. The Donets Basin (Donbas) is the principal producing district. New discoveries in Siberia in recent years have redistributed and changed the structure of the Soviet coal industry.

coal basins

Five basins account today for about 60 per cent of the known reserves of coal and lignite and more than 80 per cent of the output. These are the Donets, Karaganda, Ekibastuz, Kuznetsk, and Pechora basins.

The *Donets Basin* is the largest high quality coking-coal-producing region in the Soviet Union. About 60 per cent of all the metallurgical coke in the U.S.S.R. is produced here. Also, this area is the source of fuel for thermal-power stations and general manufacturing.

One of the richest coal basins with large reserves of high quality coking coal is the *Karaganda Basin*. Overall reserves of the basin are placed at 51 billion tons of basically coking coals low in phosphorus and sulfur.[3]

Northeast of Karaganda are the *Ekibastuz* bituminous coal deposits and the Maikubinsk brown coal deposits. Directly south of Karaganda, in the Churubai-Nurinsk and Tenteksk districts, large reserves of low-ash coking coal have been discovered.

The *Kuznetsk* (Kuzbas) coal field is the second major producer of coal in the U.S.S.R. and one of the largest centers of fuel supply for western and eastern Siberia, the Urals area, and Central Asia. The Kuznetsk field is characterized by a high ratio of coal to strata; it has about 30 working seams with aggregate thickness up to 80 meters. Thickness in some cases reaches 18 meters to 20 meters. A considerable part of the basin is suitable for strip-mining methods. Kuznetsk coals vary greatly in quality; coals of all types range from brown coals to anthracite. More than 30 per cent of the measured reserves of the basin are coking coals.

---

[2]Bureau of the Census. *The Soviet Mineral-Fuels Industries, 1928-1958, A Statistical Survey,* by D. B. Shimkin.

[3]U.S. Bureau of Mines, *International Coal Trade,* 1957, vol. 26, no. 12, December, 1957, p. 18.

The *Pechora Basin* is in the northeastern part of European U.S.S.R., largely within the boundaries of the Komi A.S.S.R. The basin contains large coal deposits, of which coking coals are especially significant. More than two-thirds of the developed reserves are in the Vorkuta and Inta deposits. The basin plays an important role in supplying fuel for industry and transport in the European north and northeast regions, wherein lies the large industrial center of Leningrad.

the coking coal problem

In general, the ascertained supply of coking coals in the U.S.S.R. is not great. Coals from many of the new mining areas of the European part of the U.S.S.R. cannot be substituted for Donets coking coals, and the only other major sources of high-quality coking coals are in the Kuznetsk and Karaganda basins, and, to a lesser extent, the Pechora Basin; all more than a thousand miles from the Donets-based steel industry. Among the undeveloped deposits, by far the most significant in size, excellence and location are those of the Chulman Basin in southern Yakutiya. Although incompletely propected they hold major promise as a coking coal base for the entire Soviet Union east of Lake Baikal.

other coal fields

Among other coal fields of local significance are the Moscow Basin, coal fields in the Urals, Central Asia, and the Minusinsk and Cheremkhovo field in eastern Siberia. A promising field for future development is the Kansk-Achinsk deposit of eastern Siberia. Easy accessibility, a seam 17 meters to 80 meters thick near the Trans-Siberian railroad, and a heat value of 3500 c/kg have made this resource a focus of current Soviet planning.

brown coal in the U.S.S.R.

The Soviet Union has reserves of brown coal, suitable for working, estimated at approximately 108,000 million tons. Brown coal basins and individual deposits are found in every part of the country. The principal brown coal deposits of the U.S.S.R. are, in the European sector, the Moscow and Dneiper; in the Urals, the Chelyabinsk, South Ural and Orsk; in Kazakhstan, the Ubagansk and Maikyubensk; in western and eastern Siberia, the Kansk-Achinsk, the Lena and others. Individual brown coal deposits are also found in the Caucasus and in parts of Middle Asia, the Baikal region, the Far East and Sakhalin Island.

Coal in India

India is fairly well supplied with coal, the deposits being confined to eastern India, in the Provinces of Assam, Bengal, Bihar, Central Provinces and Hyderabad. Some of the deposits in Godavari and Mahanadi Valleys have not been fully investigated and their extent is not known. In addition there are lignite deposits in the coastal regions of Madras and Travancore, and in Bikaner (Rajputana). The principal producing fields are Assam, West Bengal, Bihar, Orissa, Madhya, Hyderabad, Pajasthan and Vindhya Pradesh. Nearly 30 per cent of current production comes from West Bengal and Bihar.

Total reserves of all types in India are estimated at 134 billion metric tons.[4] The principal known reserves are located in the Raniganj fields (Bengal and Bihar) and the Jharia field (Bihar).

Other coal fields are in Madhya Pradesh and Andhra Pradesh States. The largest lignite deposit is in Madras State. Concentration of much of the coal output in a small area of northeast India adds to the price of coal in south and west India.

Adequate supplies of coal of metallurgical grade appear to be a critical factor in India's industrial economy. Only 4.6 billion tons are classified as "prime" coking coal and 26 billion tons as blendable coal.[5] The realization that the country's reserves of metallurgical coal were inadequate and their conservation was urgent led to the enactment of laws under which the central government was empowered to take such measurse as were necessary for the conservation[6] of this type of coal. Under an expanding industrial economy, demand for coking coal is going up. To help conserve India's reserves of coking coal and to better use the available supplies, it has been decided to use a blend of 75 per cent Raniganj coal and 25 per cent Jharia. Coal produced at the Raniganj is weakly coking but is sufficiently clean as mined, while the Jharia product is strongly coking but must be thoroughly cleaned before coking.

Coal in China

Coal reserves of mainland China definitely rank among the foremost in the world along with those of the United States and the Soviet Union. According to published reports, coal reserves amount to 1000 billion metric tons. This figure is a possible or inferred estimate and at greater depths than are now being worked.[7] Coal production in the post World

[4]U.S. Bureau of Mines, *Minerals Yearbook, 1963,* vol. IV, p. 1324.
[5]*International Coal Trade,* vol. 35, no. 11, p. 11, November, 1966.
[6]*International Coal Trade,* vol. 26, no. 8, p. 18, August, 1957.
[7]U.S. Bureau of Mines, *International Coal Trade,* vol. 27, no. 4, April, 1958.

War II period rose from a low of 20 million short tons in 1946 to an estimated 320 million short tons in 1964.[8] Seven coal-mining centers (Fushan, Fuhsin, Karlan, Huainan, Hokang, Chihsi and Tatung) each produce more than 10 million metric tons of coal. In addition, there are a considerable number of mines, each producing from one to ten million tons yearly. Recent exploration has uncovered large coal beds in central, south, southwest and northwest China, which hitherto, unlike north China and Manchuria, have been considered inadequate in coal for large scale industrial development.[9]

Japan

Japan's coal mining industry does not have the capacity to meet internal requirements. Coal production reached a high point of 61 million tons in 1961 and thereafter registered a slow decline. Japan depends heavily on imports of coking coal for her iron and steel industry. The principal contributors are the United States and Australia, the former supplying low-ash, high quality coking coal with which the higher ash, lower cost Australian coke is blended to make a metallurgical coke.

Republic of South Africa

The known coal reserves of South Africa total some 25 billion tons. In addition to this, there is an estimated 50 billion tons which have not been examined in detail.[10] The proved and indicated reserves comprise more than 80 per cent of the coal reserves of Africa. The coal fields are widely distributed geographically, in Orange Free State, Natal and Transvaal. The Natal fields supply coking coal for South African metallurgical industries. These fields also supply anthracite and semi-anthracite.

South African coal is among the cheapest in the world because of relatively low-cost labor and because the coal seams are thick and flat and occur at shallow depths. Output approximates 50 million tons annually. Coal supplies the major portion of South Africa's total energy requirements. Not only does it provide a fuel for railroads, electric power plants and manufacturing, it is also the raw material for the manufacture of liquid fuel. With the expansion of industry in the nation, coal requirements will tend to increase.

---

[8]U.S. Bureau of Mines, *Minerals Yearbook, 1964,* p. 157.

[9]U.S. Bureau of Mines, *Mineral Trade Notes,* Spec. Supp. No. 59, vol. 50, no. 3, March, 1960.

[10]U.S. Bureau of Mines, *Minerals Yearbook, 1963,* vol. IV, p. 1109.

Coal is exported in relatively limited quantities to Western Europe, and other African nations. South Africa would find a ready market in Europe to replace the more expensive American coals if transportation difficulties could be overcome. The Natal collieries are 200 to 275 miles from the port of Durban, and those in the Transvaal are more than 300 miles from the port of Lourenço Marques. Moreover, adequate railway facilities and an efficient coal harbor are lacking at present.

Rhodesia

The Wankie Colliery is the sole coal producer in Rhodesia. The principal market for Rhodesian coal is the copper industry in Zambia.

Coal in Australia

The major coal fields of Australia lie on or close to the eastern seaboard. The concentrations of coal extend from the vicinity of Sydney northward and to some extent inland to Collinsville in Queensland about 1200 miles to the north. The situation in New South Wales is one of vast reserves in flat-lying, thick seams of bituminous coal readily accessible to the seaboard.

Queensland has large reserves in thick seams, some of high quality but some distance from industrial locations and from tidewater. Victoria has large reserves of brown coal which is used mainly for electric power production. The Joint Coal Board of Australia estimates coal reserves as follows:

	Millions of Tons
New South Wales	3,000
Queensland	1,250
Victoria (brown coal)	18,000[11]
Western Australia	48

The coking coal reserves are estimated at 1000 million tons in New South Wales and 250 million tons in Queensland. In addition to an expanding need for coal in the domestic market there is a mounting export trade to Japan for hard coking coal and for coals suitable for blending.

---

[11]Available at present.

Chapter 5

Petroleum and Natural Gas

Petroleum, in the process of refining, yields gasoline, kerosene, distillate, residual fuel oil, lubricants, petroleum coke, asphalt, road oil, and feed stocks for the petrochemical industries. Gasoline is primarily used for motor fuel and, in the United States, constitutes about 40 per cent of all refined products. Distillate ranks next in volume of output and is the fuel used principally for domestic and commercial heating, railroad diesel fuel, and bunkering. There are other minor uses. Altogether, distillate represents about 20 per cent of products output. Residual oil is a heavy product of the refining process and is more nearly a competitor of coal. It finds an outlet as a fuel for large heating units, electric utility fuel, bunkering, and consumption for the armed forces. Kerosene is produced in relatively small quantities, and is used principally for range oil and tractor fuel. Lubricants from petroleum play an important role in a power-based economy. With minor exceptions, only lubricants from petroleum can withstand the high temperatures of the internal combustion engine without breaking down and losing their lubricating properties.

the markets for petroleum and its products

The world market for the products of petroleum is about 10.5 billion barrels, of which 9 billion is credited to the world outside of the Sino-Soviet area. This consumption trend will no doubt continue upwards. Demand for petroleum products was as follows in 1965.
Almost 80 percent of demand is in North America and Western Europe. If Japan, the leading industrial nation of Asia, is included the total rises to 83 per cent.

TABLE 5.1

World Market for Petroleum Products

Area	Quantity in millions of barrels
Anglo America	4,668
Western Europe	2,746
South and Middle America	640
Middle East	285
Africa	214
Asiatic area	1,115
World Total (excl. of Sino-Soviet area	9,670
Sino-Soviet area	1,647
World Total	11,318

the oil reserves of the United States

Estimates of the oil reserves of the United States have been made from time to time by U.S.G.S. officials, by oil company representatives, and by other interested parties. To date no less than fourteen such estimates have been published, varying from 145 million barrels in 1955 to 590 million barrels in 1961.[1,2] The wide variation in estimates indicates that attempts to determine the quantity of oil in existence are grossly in error.

A more satisfactory approach to an evaluation of the oil producing capabilities of the United States is to be found in the annual reports of the American Petroleum Institute.[3] The meaning of "proved reserves" as used in the API report needs to be clearly understood. The following is a partial quotation from the definition of the term "proved reserves of crude oil" as used in the annual report.

> The reserves listed in this Report, as in all previous Annual Reports, refer solely to "proved" reserves. These are the quantities of crude oil

[1]National Academy of Sciences, National Research Council, 1962, *Energy Resources,* Publication 1000-D, 141 pp.

[2]Moore, C. L. (1962) *Method for Evaluating Crude Oil Resources and Projecting Domestic Crude Oil Availability,* U.S. Dept. of Interior, Office of Oil and Gas, Washington, D.C.

[3]American Petroleum Institute. *Proved Reserves of Crude Oil, Natural Gas Liquids and Natural Gas* (annual).

which geological and engineering data demonstrate with reasonable certainty to be recoverable in the future from known oil reservoirs under existing economic and operating conditions. They represent strictly technical judgments, and are not knowingly influenced by attitudes of conservatism or optimism.

Each year's report presents data in the manner as shown for the year 1966 as an example.

TABLE 5.2

Changes in Liquid Hydrocarbon Reserves in the United States for the Year 1966

Total proved reserves of crude oil as of December 31, 1965		31, 352, 391
Additions to proved reserves in 1966:		
Revisions of previous estimates	1, 839, 307	
Extensions of old pools	814, 249	
New reserves discovered in new fields	160, 384	
New reserves discovered in new pools in old fields	150, 038	
Total proved reserves added in 1966		+ 2, 963, 978
Total		34, 316, 369
Less production during 1966		- 2, 864, 242
Total proved reserves of crude oil as of December 31, 1966		31, 452, 127
Net change in proved reserves during 1966		+ 99, 736
Additional Information:		
Indicated additional reserve as of December 31, 1966		7, 594, 019
Total original oil-in-place estimated as of December 31, 1966		380, 867, 114
Total ultimate recovery estimated as of December 31, 1966		112, 058, 863
Cumulative production as of December 31, 1966		80, 606, 736

In addition to the data on estimated crude oil reserves, revised annually, the American Petroleum Institute also estimates the reserves of natural gas liquids in the same manner as the crude oil reserves.

The totals for crude oil and natural gas liquids are combined and presented in Table 5.3, showing "Total Liquid Hydrocarbons."

TABLE 5.3

Total Liquid Hydrocarbons

(Thousands of Barrels of 42 U.S. Gallons)

Total proved reserves as of December 31, 1965.		286,468,923
Extensions and revisions of previous estimate during the year of 1966	14,198,707	
New reserves discovered in 1966	6,021,725	
Net changes in underground storage during 1966.	134,523	
Total proved reserves added and net changes in underground storage during 1966		20,354,955
Total proved reserves as of December 31, 1965 and additions during 1966		306,823,878
Deduct production during 1966.		17,491,073
Total proved reserves of natural gas as of December 31, 1966		289,332,805

NATURAL GAS LIQUIDS RESERVES

(Thousands of Barrels of 42 U.S. Gallons)

Total proved reserves as of December 31, 1965.		8,023,534
Extensions and resviions of previous estimate during year of 1966	765,816	
New reserves discovered in 1966	128,300	
Total proved reserves added in 1966		894,116
Total proved reserves as of December 31, 1965 and new proved reserves added in 1966		8,917,650
Deduct production during 1966.		588,684
Total proved reserves of natural gas liquids as of December 31, 1966		8,328,966

In estimating the future trend of oil discovery, the year-to-year behavior of the last item in the summary, "change in crude oil reserves," is particularly interesting. In the period from 1946 to 1966, the annual change in crude oil reserves was upward for all but four years. The total reserve picture increased from 21 billion barrels in 1946 to 31 billion barrels in 1965. Since 1957, there have been four years when losses in reserves were recorded or a trend toward declining annual growth or losses. This behavior will become significant if the trend continues for a long period. A long continued decline of discoveries below production would be an indication that the petroleum industry of the nation cannot continue to meet oil demand from domestic sources by reason of (a) inadequate exploration activity, (b) higher finding costs, (c) competition of imported oil.

geographical distribution of the industry

The resource base of the North American oil industry is the broad sedimentary basin which extends from the Gulf of Mexico to the Arctic Ocean. Within this basin are several fairly well-defined districts within which the geologic structure is favorable for the accumulation of oil. Texas leads in both current production and estimated reserves. The principal well-defined districts in Texas are the Gulf Coast, east Texas, west Texas, the Panhandle, and other districts. Louisiana, Oklahoma, New Mexico and Kansas follow in order of output. About 70 per cent of the nation's oil comes from the Gulf Coast and Mid-Continent fields. In the mountain states, Wyoming leads, followed by Montana, Colorado, and Utah.

On the West Coast, oil and gas occur in California and Washington but important fields are limited to the southern part of California. Four important districts are San Joaquin, Santa Maria, Ventura, and the Los Angeles basin. California is third in production among the states.

Small quantities of oil are also produced in the Appalachian states and the eastern interior states of Indiana and Illinois.

The continental shelves of the world have tremendous areas and include large volumes of oil bearing sands. Offshore production along the Louisiana and Texas Gulf Coast and in California is becoming important.

Oil and natural gas production in Alaska is located principally in the vicinity of Cook Inlet and on the Kenai Peninsula. The most productive is the Swanson River field. Production is running about 10 million barrels a year, but there is not enough information to make an estimate of future possibilities.

Canada

When the Leduc oil field in Canada was discovered in 1947, Canada entered the group of important oil producers. Before this discovery,

Canada produced only small amounts of oil in Ontario and southern Alberta. Under the urgency of World War II needs in the Alaskan theater of operations, wells were drilled in the vicinity of Norman and carried by pipeline to Whitehorse for refining. After the discovery of the large Leduc field, other large pools were discovered which extended beyond the boundaries of Alberta into Saskatchewan, southwest Manitoba, and northeast British Columbia. In these provinces, from the Rocky Mountain front to the pre-Cambrian shield, and from the international boundary to the Arctic Ocean, is a vast sedimentary basin which covers about 600,000 square miles. Approximately one-quarter of this area, along the eastern boundary, is only thinly covered with sediments and unfavorable for oil accumulation. The main body of the basin, however, covers 475,000 square miles and ranks as prospective oil territory.

Athabaska tar sands

The hydrocarbon resources of North America may someday be supplemented from the vast deposits of oil sands (also referred to as tar sands and bituminous sands) along the Athabaska River in northeastern Alberta. The deposits cover an area of 10,000 to 30,000 square miles and range from a few feet to more than 200 feet in thickness. The oil content of these sands is estimated to range from 1 to 25 per cent and the reserve is placed variously from 100 billion barrels to as high as 600 billion.[4]

oil shale

Oil shale in some amount or other is found in 29 states of the Union, but only the shales in Colorado, Utah and Wyoming have been considered to have potential commercial significance. More than four-fifths of the material in these three states is in Colorado alone. The oil-forming material in oil shale is a solid organic substance called *kerogen.* The oil shale deposits in these three states are estimated by the Department of the Interior to contain more than 1000 billion barrels of petroleum-like material that can be converted into products similar to or identical with those obtained from petroleum. About 530 billion barrels are in beds 15 feet or more thick that average 25 gallons of oil to a ton of shale.

Although considerable research has been expended on the recovery of oil from shale and a pilot plant has been in operation, the cost of

---

[4]Hubbert M. King: National Academy of Sciences. National Research Council. 1962, Energy Resources, Publication 1000-D.

extracting oil from shale has prevented it from becoming commercially competitive with petroleum. Continued research in the technology of oil shale processing and rising costs of locating new reserves of oil and gas may ultimately result in adding shale oil to the existing sources of energy.

foreign oil supplies

The United States became an importer of oil in 1948 and it has remained in that category ever since. Overseas oil is plentiful and the landed price on the East Coast is substantially below the delivered price of comparable domestic crudes. That this is the case has made it attractive for corporations in the United States to seek oil sources in foreign nations. The principal contributing nations or areas of crude oil are Canada, South America (Venezuela and Colombia), the Persian Gulf area (Iran, Kuwait, the Neutral Zone, Qatar, Saudi Arabia), North Arica, (Libya, Algeria, U.A.R.) and Sumatra.

The principal sources of refined products are Netherlands Antilles, Trinidad and Tobago, and Venezuela.

the role of the Caribbean in the world oil industry

The Caribbean area includes Venezuela, Colombia, Trinidad and Tobago, Curacoa, and Aruba. The latter two islands of the Netherlands Antilles are included because of their large refining facilities. Venezuela produces more than 90 per cent of the output of this area; Colombia and Trinidad are only minor contributors. Venezuela, therefore, determines the pattern of oil distribution and trade. The local market for Caribbean oil output is minor. The function of oil production in this area is that of a supplier of petroleum and oil products to North American and European markets. Shipments to Latin America, Africa, and Asia are minor by comparison. Both crude petroleum and refined products are exported from Venezuela, either directly or by way of refineries located on the islands of Curacao, Aruba, and Trinidad. In both the North American market and in Europe, the receipts of refined products from Venezuela directly or via the island refineries exceeds the quantities of crude petroleum received.

There are two major oil producing districts in Venezuela. Western Venezuela comprises the important Lake Maracaibo Basin, and the neighboring Zúlia, Falcón, and Barinas basins. Altogether, they yield about 80 per cent of Venezuela's output. The other important producing district is Eastern Venezuela, mainly in the states of Anzoátegui, Monágas, and Guárico, lying between the Orinoco River and the Caribbean Gulf Coast.

Trinidad is more important as an oil refining state than a producer of oil. Crude oil production accounts for only 3 per cent of the total for all Latin America but refinery output is about 10 per cent for the same area.

Argentina and Colombia each produce small quantities of oil. In Colombia the principal oil producing areas are found in two districts, the Magdalena Basin and the Colombian portion of the Maracaibo Basin.

Mexico

Mexico produces between 3 and 4 per cent of the oil output of the North American continent and 1 per cent of the world total. Mexican oil resources occur in a number of fields closely bordering the Gulf of Mexico. The nation is divided into five distinct oil producing zones: Northeast, Tampico, Poza Rica, Veracruz, and southern Yucatan. The northeast zone, surrounding Reynosa, contains almost exclusively natural gas deposits. Reynosa field is the largest and most important among the fields.

The Tampico-Poza area is by far the most important as well as the oldest Mexican producing area. This area includes four groups of fields. Together they produce over 60 per cent of the total output.

Discoveries in the Veracruz zone have to date been few and with limited reserves. The main field in the area is Angostura.

The southern zone is second after Tampico-Poza Rica in petroleum importance. Oil stems mainly from the recent fields near Villahermosa. Mexico's Yucatan Peninsula is still in the early state of exploration.

the oil industry in Western Europe

Western Europe is the largest consumer of oil and oil products next to the United States. Domestic sources of petroleum, on the other hand, are meager, and account for only a small fraction of the total demand for crude oil and imported oil products.

The geographic pattern of the oil industry in Europe is determined by the source of crude oil supply. The main suppliers in order of importance are the Persian Gulf nations, North Africa, Venezuela, and minor quantities from other sources. Among the Persian Gulf nations or sheikdoms, the leader is Kuwait, followed by Iraq, Saudi Arabia and Iran. Others contribute lesser amounts.

In North Africa, the rapid rise in output of Algeria and Libya is contributing heavily to the European markets. Venezuela finds its principal outlet in the British Isles and the Atlantic Seaboard nations of France, West Germany, and the Netherlands.

About 90 per cent of oil shipments into Western Europe consist of crude petroleum and the remainder of refined products.

The Transportation System of the Western European Oil Industry

Oil moves to the Western European markets from the sources of production via pipeline, Suez Canal, the Mediterranean, the Atlantic Ocean, and around the Cape of Good Hope.

Crude oil pipelines in Europe originate from tidewater points on the Atlantic Seaboard and the Mediterranean ports and proceed inland to the several industrial centers. Among the principal lines noted are Wilhelmshaven to Cologne, 24″; Rotterdam to Rhine, 24″; Marseille to Mannheim, 34″; Rhine to Danube, 26″; Pegli (Genoa) to Neustadt, 26″; Trieste to Neustadt, 40″. There are, in addition to these, several short lines from coastal points inland and, in addition, several lines proposed or in building.

There are also, in addition to the crude oil lines, a number of product lines used for the distribution of refined products to market destinations.

Six ocean or deep sea water routes transport oil to the European continent. They are

1. The pipeline-Mediterranean route from Saudi Arabia and Iraq to the shores of the Levant and by tanker to European termini. The capacity of this route is limited by the carrying capacity of the Trans-Arabian Pipeline from Saudi Arabia and the pipelines from Iraq. This route also has the disadvantage of traversing several Arabian nations or sheikdoms with the almost certain possibility of the imposition of transit taxes, not to mention shutdowns.
2. The water route from the Persian Gulf area through the Suez Canal to European Mediterranean ports. The canal can now handle fully loaded tankers with a capacity of 60,000 DWT. Transit by oil tankers is an exceedingly valuable source of revenue to the U.A.R. government since about three-fourths of the canal movement is oil. The Suez Canal Authority is reported to be making plans to widen and deepen the canal to handle fully loaded oil tankers of 48-foot draft and 112,000 DWT.[5] The hazards of this route became evident

[5]*New York Times,* July 29, 1966.

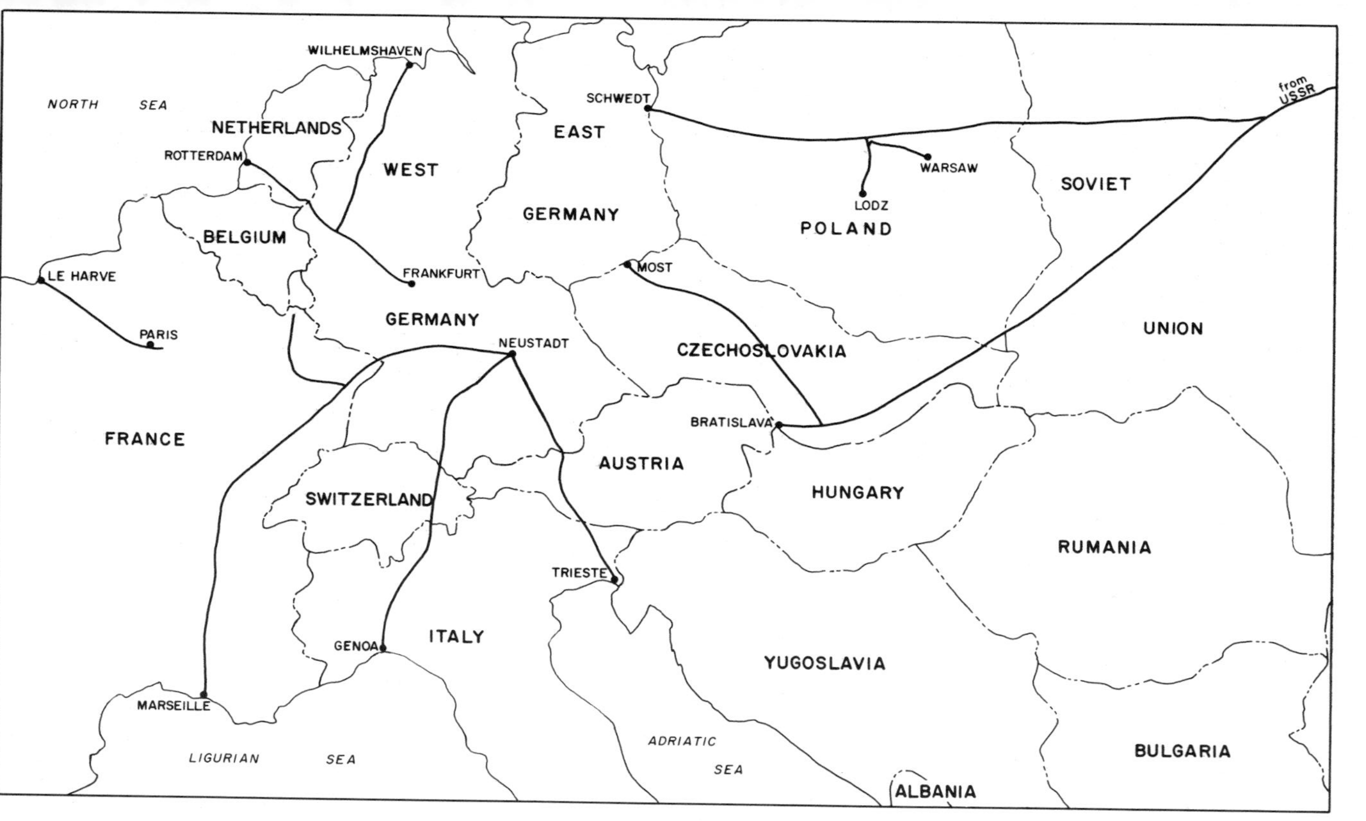

FIGURE 5.1 Major Crude Oil Pipelines in Europe

with the shutdown of the canal in June, 1967, during the U.A.R.-Israeli war.

3. The intra-Mediterranean route from North African producers. The only restrictions on the size of tankers used on this route are the capacities of the ports of origin and destination. Moreover, it is the shortest of all routes and, therefore, the lowest in cost.
4. The Cape of Good Hope route from the Persian Gulf area to destinations in the United Kingdom and Atlantic ports of Western Europe offers low cost transportation of petroleum in the tankers of 85,000 DWT or larger.
5. The route from Venezuela to Western Europe supplies mainly the United Kingdom, West Germany, the Netherlands, France, and Norway.
6. Internal transportation by barges over inland waterways complements transportation by pipeline.

In conclusion, Western Europe is next to the United States in the consumption of petroleum products. Originally, an almost exclusively coal-based economy, the proportion of oil products as a source of fuel is growing. With it is an increasing dependence upon oil sources beyond the borders of the continent. Fortunately, competition among several producers acts as a restraint on the danger of interruption of supply. Moreover, oil and gas developments in the North Sea may prove to be so extensive as to become a significant contributor to Europe's needs.

petroleum in the Middle East

Middle East oil is a major element in the economies of Europe and the East. It is one of the keys to the industrial future of Western Europe and necessary to the growth of European economy. The group of oil producing states and sheikdoms collectively grouped as the Middle East now produce a quantity of oil equal to the output of the United States and one-fourth of the world's total. By a conservative estimate the area is credited with 70 per cent of the world's reserves with Kuwait as the most important. Saudi Arabia and Iran are also high in rank. The estimate as of January 1, 1965, is given in Table 5.4.

The nations and sheikdoms in the Middle East as producers, in order of importance, are Kuwait, Saudi Arabia, Iran, Iraq, Neutral Zone, Qatar, and the Trucial States. In addition to the producing states, the nations of Jordan, Syria, and Lebanon are interested because of pipeline transit across their territories and the United Arab Republic is interested because of tanker transit through the Suez Canal.

TABLE 5.4

Middle East Oil Reserves

Middle East Oil Reserves	
Kuwait	68,700,000
Saudi Arabia	66,000,000
Iran	44,200,000
Iraq	24,000,000
Libya	20,000,000
Neutral Zone	13,000,000
Abu Dhabi	12,500,000
Algeria	7,250,000
Qatar	4,000,000
Nigeria	3,500,000
Syria	1,500,000
Turkey	1,000,000
Tunisia	300,000
Bahrain	200,000

Grouping of Oil Fields

The oil fields of Saudi Arabia, Kuwait, and the Neutral Zone are, under present development, adjacent to or in close proximity to the Persian Gulf. The Iranian fields are a short distance inland and the Iraqi fields, with the exception of Zubair, are in the deep interior.

Kuwait

Kuwait is the leading petroleum-producing country of the Persian Gulf area. It is second only to Venezuela in volume of petroleum exports. In addition nearly one-fourth of the world's proved petroleum reserve is in Kuwait. Low-cost ocean transportation of oil is of particular interest to the Sheikdom of Kuwait. Her markets are Western Europe, mainly, but also the United States, Japan, and other lesser users. Her productive wells are practically on tidewater. Her oil export is entirely by tanker, unhampered by any transit over neighboring countries. Her port is equipped to load three 100,000 DWT tankers simultaneously. Her crude petroleum can reach all major markets via the Cape of Good Hope to the West and the Malacca Straits to Japan and California at competitive transport costs with smaller tankers over the Suez-Mediterranean route or the Tapline-Mediterranean route.

The Neutral Zone

The Kuwait-Saudi Arabia Neutral Zone was established by treaty in 1892 as a solution to the boundary problem then existing between the two countries. The area is about 6400 square miles of which 2400 is offshore in the Persian Gulf. In this area, Kuwait and Saudi Arabia each have an undivided half-interest. The Zone ranks fifth in petroleum production in the Middle East. Two American companies hold leases onshore and the Japanese-owned Arabian Oil Company has leases in the Persian Gulf beyond the 6-mile limit.

The Neutral Zone has no overland pipeline connections and must depend entirely on ocean transportation.

Saudi Arabia

Saudi Arabia currently ranks immediately below Kuwait in production among the Middle East states. The petroleum industry has dominated the national economy, providing almost all government revenue, foreign exchange earnings, and industrial employment. The major producing fields are Ghawar, Abqaiq, Safaniya, Khursaniyah, and Abu Hadriya. The refinery at Ras Tanuras has a capacity of 255,000 barrels daily.

Oil from Saudi Arabia is shipped to Europe by tanker through the Suez Canal or around the Cape of Good Hope, and by Trans-Arabian Pipeline across Saudi Arabia, Jordan, Syria, and Lebanon to Sidon.

Iraq

The Iraqi nation has two groups of oil producing fields: the Zubair and associated fields at the head of the Persian Gulf, and the northerly land-locked fields of which the principal producer is Kirkuk. About 80 per cent of the oil output comes from the northern field of Kirkuk and associated fields, and the remainder from the Zubair-Ramaila field. There are small contributions from other fields. Oil shipments from the Kirkuk field must be carried 550 miles by pipeline to the Mediterranean Coast. One 12″, one 16″, and one 30″ pipeline each connect the

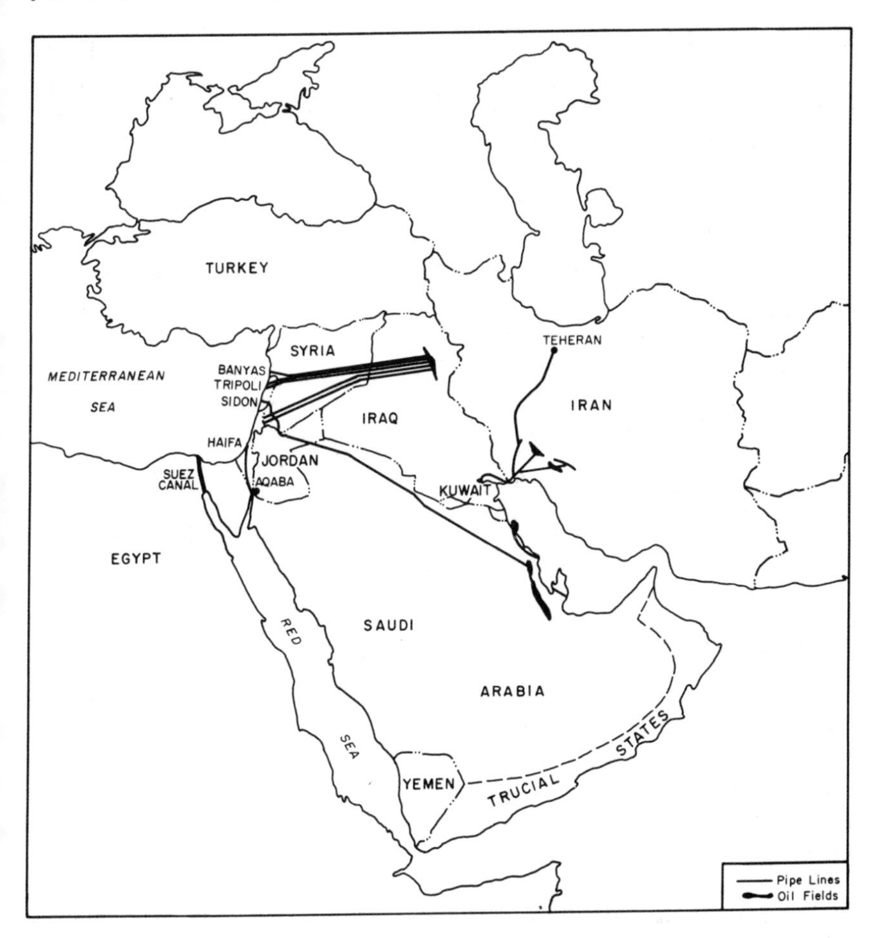

FIGURE 5.2 Pipelines in the Middle East

Kirkuk field with Tripoli in Lebanon and Baniyas in Syria. Petroleum from the Zubair-Ramaila field is carried 65 miles by pipeline to the deepwater loading terminal at Khor-al-Amaya at the port of Basra on the Persian Gulf.

Iran

Middle East oil history began in Iran when an Englishman, William D'Arcy, opened the famous Masjid-i-Sulaiman (Temple of Solomon Pool) in 1908. The proven oil fields, with one exception, are on the low flat plains on the southwestern border of Iran, at the foothills of the Zagros

Mountains. There are seven fields, all connected with the refinery at Abadan. A small field, Alborz, near the community of Qum, was discovered and opened by the government-owned National Iranian Oil Company. Much of Iranian petroleum is refined at the large refinery at Abadan.

Kharg Island

An oil terminal designed to handle all Iranian Consortium crude exports has been constructed on this island 25 miles off the coast. The terminal can accommodate ten modern tankers simultaneously, including vessels of more than 200,000 DWT. To feed the terminal, two crude oil pipelines have been built from inland fields, connecting with submarine pipelines running from the coast to the island.

The Minor Middle East Producers

Bahrein Island, off the Saudi Arabian Coast, has a small output of oil from one field. More important is the refinery located on the island with pipeline connections to several oil fields on mainland Saudi Arabia. The pipelines from Saudi Arabia to the Bahrein refinery have a throughput capacity of 200,000 barrels daily. The Bahrein refinery annually accounts for 17 per cent of petroleum products produced in the Middle East and 25 per cent of the exports.

Qatar is the largest among the minor producers. All Qatar production is exported except for a minor quantity which is refined for local consumption.

The *Trucial Coast* is the most recent addition to the petroleum producing areas of the Middle East. Commencing production in 1962, output exceeded that of Bahrein Island the next year and is still trending upward.

Israel has a small production and a refinery at Haifa, which receives crude petroleum from Iran via the Red Sea and the Gulf of Aqaba.

North Africa

The recent entry of Libya and Algeria among the major producers in the Middle East has introduced a new dimension in the petroleum supply situation for Western European nations. While it is true that the Persian Gulf nations have adequate supplies of petroleum to meet European needs for an indefinite future, the short distance from northern Africa across the Mediterranean Sea and the absence of potential bottlenecks to free movement of vessels (as in the case of the Suez Canal) will favor the North African nations as contenders for the European market.

The North African oil producing nations are, comparatively speaking, newcomers. Algeria entered the field in 1955 and Libya followed in 1961. The U.A.R. bids fair to become an important producer with the recent discovery of a large well in the western part of the country. Cumulative reserves are currently estimated at 10 billion barrels and it is likely that discovery of new fields will increase this figure.

Algeria and Libya

Algeria began as an oil producer in 1955 with an output of 438,000 barrels and in the ensuing decade production rose to 201 million barrels and cumulative output to 754 million barrels. The principal producing districts are the Polignac Basin of the Sahara and the Triassic Basin to the northwest. Pipelines extend from the Polignac Basin to Skhirra in Tunisia and from the Hassi Messaoud and adjoining fields to Bougie on the Algerian Mediterranean Coast. New discoveries of oil deposits continue to be reported and, as in the case of Libya, the ultimate reserve is still undetermined. As of 1965, it is reported as 7.4 billion barrels. The output is now limited by pipeline capacity. Algeria exports crude oil principally to France, West Germany, Italy and the Netherlands.

Libya has made the most rapid strides in petroleum production since June 1959 when the Zelten field was opened. Since then several new pools or fields have been opened and three pipelines built from fields to ports on the Mediterranean. Pipeline distances are shorter and depth of wells is less than in Algeria, thus giving to Libya a slight competitive advantage. Libya exports crude oil to West Germany, the United Kingdom, Italy, the Netherlands, France, Spain, and the United States, in the order named.

Central and South Africa

Among the several nations of Africa below the Sahara, *Nigeria* is the only one of moderate oil-producing significance. Crude petroleum was first produced in 1958, with an output of 1,978,000 barrels and reached 44 million barrels in 1964. Proven reserves are estimated at 3 billion barrels, but it is likely that reserve figures will continue to increase in view of extensive exploration, both on land and offshore.

In addition to petroleum, Nigeria also produces natural gas. The gas is supplied to run the power station at Afam, and for other industrial uses.

petroleum in the U.S.S.R.

The Union of Soviet Socialist Republics ranks as one of the important oil producing nations of the world. It is exceeded only by the United States and the states closely grouped around the Persian Gulf. Commercial production in the Soviet Union began in 1873 with an output of about 1000 barrels in the Baku field. Because of easy finding and prolific yields, Russian oil development was confined from an early date almost exclusively to the Caucasus region, thus excluding from attention other vast areas of promise. As late as 1950, the Caucasus region and the Baku field alone contributed more than half of the oil output of the Soviet Union. By 1965, the Baku field had produced more than 6 billion barrels of oil.

Beginning in the late thirties, exploration activities disclosed several new oil bearing districts, namely:

1. The Azerbaijan fields (Baku) already discussed.
2. The Volga-Urals field.
3. The Emba fields.
4. The Turkmen fields.
5. The Tyumen territory in the West Siberian Lowland.

The Volga-Urals, sometimes referred to as the "Second Baku," is now the focal point of the U.S.S.R.'s expanding oil industry. This producing area, between the Volga River and the Ural Mountains, furnishes more than 70 per cent of Soviet crude oil production. Three areas in the Volga-Urals—the Tatar Republic, the Bashkir Republic and the Kuibyshev region—have each surpassed Baku in output. "Second Baku" holds an important geographical advantage over other major oil producing regions. Unlike the Caucasus, Trans-Caspian, and Sakhalin areas, it is fairly well located for consuming centers.

The Emba fields lie south of the Volga-Urals district, near Gurev. The north-south extension of the district is about 400 miles, down to the north shore of the Caspian Sea.

East of the Caspian Sea are the Turkmen fields in the vicinity of Krasnovodsk. In the West Siberian Lowland, in the vicinity of Tyumen, where oil was first struck in 1960, the field is reported to contain economic reserves of billions of barrels, large enough to call the region the "Third Baku." In the Far East, Sakhalin Island has long been an oil producer.

Soviet Oil Transportation Patterns

The Soviets use sea and river transportation, rail, and pipeline for the movements of crude petroleum, refined products and natural gas.

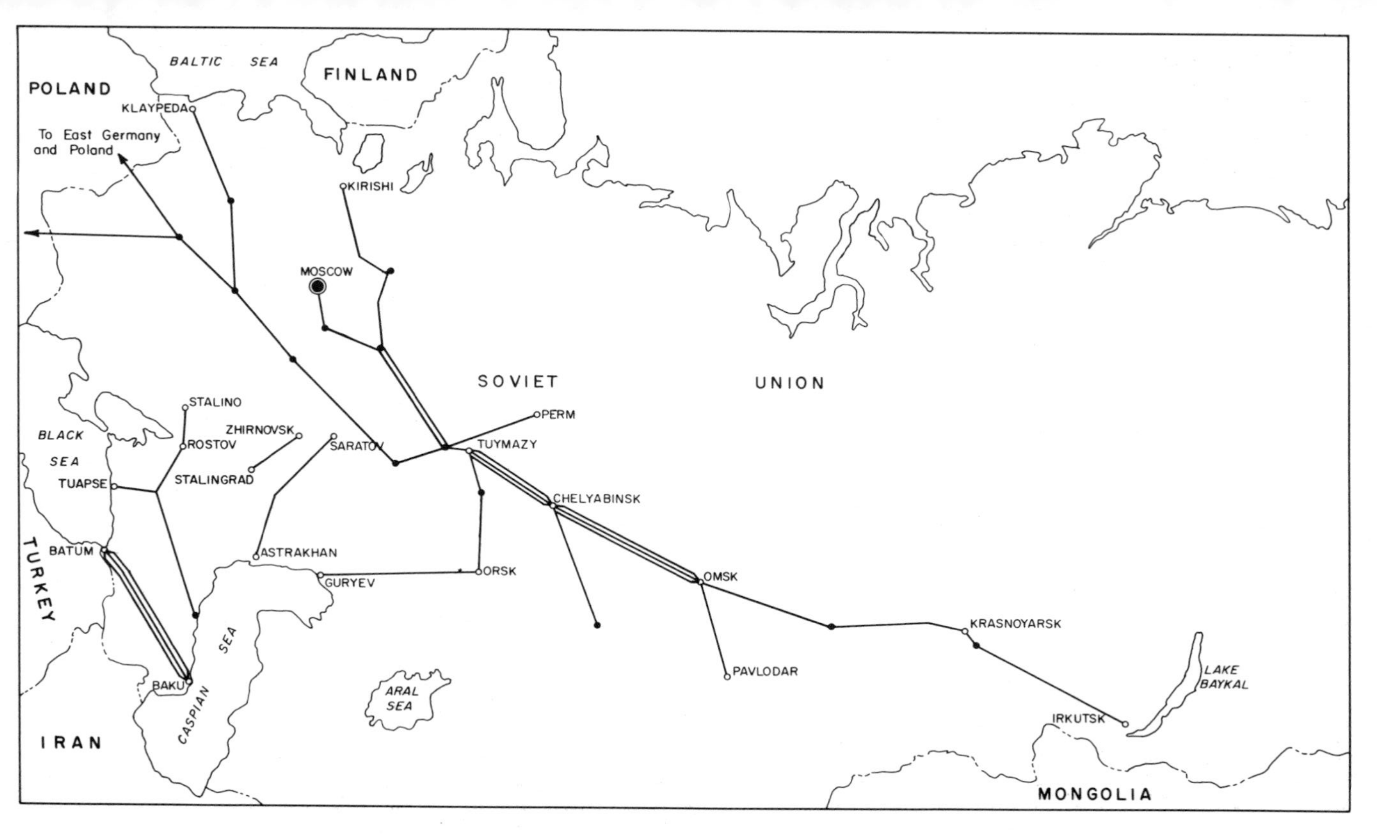

FIGURE 5.3 Oil Pipelines in the U.S.S.R.

The relative importance of water movements declined sharply from about 44 per cent in 1940, particularly in the case of Caspian Sea movements as production shifted from Baku to the inland fields of the Volga-Urals. Rail movements continue to be important. However, pipeline movements show the greatest increase. Two major pipeline developments may be noted in this connection. One is the so-called Comecon line from Kuybyshev to Pland, East Germany, Czechoslovakia and Hungary, a distance of about 3000 miles. A branch of the Comecon line from Unecha to Ventspils on the Baitic Sea via Polotsk enables the Soviets to enter Western European markets by tanker. Eastward a 2400 mile Trans-Siberian pipeline from Tuymazy, in the Volga-Urals fields, transports oil to the Angarsk refinery near Irkutsk.

the Far East

Four areas, Indonesia, India, Brunei and Burma, produce petroleum. Only Indonesia has an output large enough to be of more than local significance. The areas in Southeast Asia where oil is being recovered, are scattered over a wide expanse. The largest islands, Borneo, Sumatra, New Guinea and Java, possess the chief oil producing areas. Indonesia produces 80 per cent of the total. About 50 per cent of the crude oil is used in the domestic market and the remainder is exported to Australia, Japan, the Philippines and the United States, and minor quantities to other Southeastern Asian nations.

China

Oil is produced in the Kansu, Dzhungaria, Tsardam, Yunnan, and Szechwan basins, all in northwest China. Oil production in 1964 was estimated at 62 million barrels, some of which was distilled from shale or coal. China's oil output, while still small, is increasing as new fields are added to developed reserve.

Natural Gas

Natural gas outranks both petroleum and coal as a source of fuel and power in the economy of the United States. In addition to a fuel supply, it is also the basis for the manufacture of carbon black, hydrogen, petrochemicals, rubber, and an imposing array of chemical products.

Where hydrogen sulfide is present, natural gas also becomes a source of sulfur. Helium is present in natural gas fields, principally those within 200 miles of Amarillo, Texas. Natural gas occurs in gas fields only, or in association with petroleum reservoirs. In the latter case it may occur as free gas in contact with crude oil in the reservoirs or gas in solution with crude oil. Associated gas fields are by far the most important of the three sources.

world industry

The outstanding natural gas producers are the United States, the U.S.S.R. and Canada. In somewhat lower rank, but important, are the European nations of Austria, France, Italy, Rumania, and the Netherlands. Outside of Europe, there is significant production in Mexico, Venezuela, Chile, Argentina, Japan, Indonesia, Saudi Arabia, Iran, Pakistan, and Algeria. Small quantities are produced in a score of other nations.

United States

In the United States, natural gas serves a wide range of markets: residential and commercial heating, field and pipeline operations, electric utility power plants, and general manufacturing.

The producing districts or states of note are Texas, Louisiana, Oklahoma, New Mexico, Kansas, and California. These six states account for 90 per cent of the natural gas output.

Natural gas is used in all but two of the states in continental United States. There are four more or less well-defined areas of natural gas consumption. The first group is in the Lower Mississippi Valley. More than one-third of all gas consumption is in Texas and the adjoining states of Louisiana, Arkansas, Oklahoma and New Mexico. Not only is the cost of gas lower in the Texas area and neighboring states than the cost of gas in other areas, but it is also lower than potentially competitive fuels.

The second area of large consumption is in the Upper Mississippi Valley, with such large metropolitan areas as Chicago, St. Louis, Minneapolis-St. Paul, Detroit, Indianapolis, and the large Ohio cities.

The third area contains the Pacific Coast states with California accounting for 90 per cent of the consumption. The fourth area is the northeastern United States embracing the Middle Atlantic and lower New England states.

Natural Gas Reserves

As of January first, 1967, natural gas reserves for the United States were estimated at 289 million million cubic feet and for Canada, 43 million million cubic feet. The procedure in estimating gas reserves is similar to that used for crude oil and a report of the current estimated reserves is issued each year. The data for the the year 1966 for both countries is shown in Tables 5.5 and 5.6.

TABLE 5.5

Natural Gas Reserves

(Millions of Cubic Feet—14.73 psia, at 60°F)

Total proved reserves of liquid hydrocarbons as of December 31, 1965		39, 375, 925
Additions to proved reserves in 1966:		
Revisions of previous estimates	2, 473, 540	
Extensions of old pools	945, 832	
New reserves discovered in new fields	213, 762	
New reserves discovered in new pools in old fields	224, 960	
Total proved reserves added in 1966		+ 3, 858, 094
Total		43, 234, 019
Less production during 1966		- 3, 452, 026
Total proved reserves of liquid hydrocarbons as of December 31, 1966		39, 781, 093
Net change in proved reserves during 1966		+ 405, 168

Canada

Canada ranks next to the United States and the U.S.S.R. in the marketed production of natural gas. The gas fields are mainly in Alberta with a few additional fields of minor importance in British Columbia and Saskatchewan. Alberta gas is carried by pipeline to Winnipeg and further eastward to Toronto. A considerable quantity is exported to the Pacific Coast states of the United States and also to Wisconsin, Minnesota and Montana.

An important by-product of the Canadian gas industry is the recovery of sulfur from hydrogen sulfide in the gas. The significance of this industry is discussed in Chapter 7. The reserves of natural gas as of January 1, 1966, were estimated at 44 million million cubic feet, from a level of 16.6 million million cubic feet in 1955. The method of estimating reserves is identical with that used in the United States.

TABLE 5.6

Marketable Natural Gas in Canada

(Millions of Cubic Feet at 14.65 psia and 60°F)

Remaining Proved Marketable Reserves at December 31, 1965		40,354,527
Revisions	2,158,536	
Extensions	1,532,317	
1966 Discoveries	512,086	
Net Change in Underground Storage during 1966	17,918	
Reserves added in 1966		4,220,857
Reserves at December 31, 1965 plus Reserves added in 1966		44,575,384
Less 1966 Net Production[1]		1,125,289
Remaining Proved Marketable Reserves at December 31, 1966		43,450,095
Change in Marketable Reserves during 1966		+3,095,568

[1] Based on Table 3, p. 26 of vol. 21 "Proved Reserves of Crude Oil, Natural Gas Liquids and Natural Gas," December 31, 1966. Report of the American Gas Association, New York.

natural gas abroad

With the discovery and development of natural gas in the North Sea and the United Kingdom, natural gas is now available in a number of countries throughout the world. The Groningen gas field in the Netherlands, discovered in 1959, ranks second only to the Hugoton-Amarillo field of Kansas and Texas, in terms of recoverable gas. Other major gas fields have been discovered in Australia, North Africa, Nigeria, Pakistan, and South America. These discoveries raise the question of the economic potential of natural gas. Still to be determined is how much of the natural gas discovered in the several nations can be utilized. The economic value of a new gas field in Canada, for example, depends on its distance from a branch line from Winnipeg through the northern lake states, which supplies Superior, Sault Ste. Marie, and Sarnia.

Transportation looms as a key factor in determining the extent to which gas deposits can be marketed. Pipeline construction involves heavy expenditures and can only be profitable if a sizable volume of gas is sent through the line.

The North Sea gas discoveries are close to consuming areas. Britain, with a population of 55 million, is practically at the doorstep of North Sea gas. Similarly, the Netherlands gas field in Groningen can serve a population of more than 50 million people within a 200-mile radius.

Outside the North Sea area, the economic potential of other gas deposits is largely limited by the economics of pipeline transportation. While there is much gas in North Africa, and even more in the Middle East, these areas are too far from the major consuming and industrial centers of Europe to justify the construction of pipelines.

In South America, long distances and difficult terrain between gas fields and consuming centers have so far limited any large-scale commercial use of that continent's gas resources. Only in Argentina, where gas fields are located within economic distance of Buenos Aires and the land is relatively flat, has any extensive use been made of pipelines to transport natural gas.

In Chile and Peru large reserves of gas have been found, but the Andes Mountains present a formidable obstacle to the connection of the gas fields to consuming centers. Venezuela, the continent's major oil producer, is flaring a large portion of her gas output due to lack of commercial markets.

Australian gas fields are close to such population centers as Brisbane, and possibly Adelaide, Sydney, and Melbourne.

Chapter **6**

Nonferrous Metals: Copper, Aluminum, Lead and Zinc

Copper

Copper is one of the few common metals that finds its greatest application in commercially pure rather than in alloyed form. The high electrical conductivity of copper, more than anything else, accounts for its widespread use in the electrical field. With the exception of small quantities of fire-refined copper, the metal is marketed in the form of electrolytically refined copper. This is 99.9 per cent copper and silver.

The copper market begins at the point at which refined copper is sold to primary fabricators and end users. Nearly 100 per cent of the refined copper is processed by the primary fabricators; the wire mills and the brass mills. They are the chief buyers.

The electrical industry consumes more copper than any other application. Construction is next, followed by transportation. Nations of the Atlantic Basin consume about 74 per cent of the world's total output. If the industrialized nations of Japan and U.S.S.R. are added, the total rises to 90 per cent. Among these nations only the United States, the U.S.S.R., and Japan are substantial producers of the metal.

The metal for the fabricators of copper products in the industrial nations noted above comes from mines remotely located from the consuming centers, and from ores of varying copper content. The average copper content is from 0.75 per cent in the United States to 1.6 to 1.9 per cent in Chile; nearly 5 per cent in the Congo (Kinshasa), and from 3 to 4.5 per cent in Zambia. In view of the low metal content of ores, it becomes imperative that copper ores be concentrated as much as possible near the mine.

The Copper Producers of the World and Their Relation to Markets

major producing areas

Four areas are outstanding in the production of the world's copper output. They are

1. The United States, Canada, and northern Mexico.
2. Chile and Peru.
3. The Copper Belt in Africa, containing parts of Zambia, Republic of the Congo, and Southern Rhodesia.
4. The Ural Mountains and the Kazakhstan region in the U.S.S.R.

The second level of copper producers, each contributing from 1 to 2 per cent of the world total, but nevertheless important locally, are Japan, Australia, Yugoslavia, the Philippines and the Republic of South Africa. Others that may be mentioned are Turkey, Spain, Sweden, Finland and East Germany.

industry in the United States

The principal sources of copper in the United States are in the western states. The mines extend from Montana in the north to Arizona and New Mexico in the south. Of the twenty-five leading copper producing mines twenty-one are in the western states, two in Michigan, and one each in Tennessee and Pennsylvania. The western mines, with a few exceptions, are designated as porphyry coppers. The essential characteristics of the deposits are their huge size, particularly with respect to horizontal dimensions; the relative uniformity with which the copper minerals are disseminated throughout the mass; and the low average per-ton copper content of the exploitable ore.

In the mountain states, Arizona has sixteen mines and has about half of the copper output of the United States. Among the well-known mining districts are Morenci, Ajo, Pima, Globe-Miami, Bisbee, Ray, Silver Bell and Bagdad. Nevada has two mines, at Ely and Yerington. Utah, at Bingham Canyon near Salt Lake City, Montana at Butte, and New Mexico each have one. Five of these mines also yield silver and gold as a by-product of the copper recovery.

Importance of the Mountain States Copper Industry

This vast district, from Butte, Montana, to Cananea, in Sonora, Mexico, is one of the important copper producing areas of the world. Since the beginning of mining to 1965, the area has produced 52 million tons of copper. Currently, it is producing about 20 per cent of the world's output. Although there are still about five underground mining districts, the trend is toward surface mining.

Michigan, the one large copper producing state outside of the western states, has two large mines. Copper production began in 1845 as native copper and reached a peak of 137,000 tons in 1916, after which it declined. Copper production received a new impetus with the opening of the White Pine mine, which now ranks as one of the ten major copper producers in the United States.

Canada

Canada ranks among the leading copper producers of the world. In output, it is exceeded only by the United States, Zambia, U.S.S.R., and Chile.

The copper of Canadian ores is associated with other base and precious metals. About 40 per cent of the copper produced is derived from copper-nickel ores and the remainder from copper-gold, copper-lead, and copper-lead-zinc ores. The average grade of ore is between 1 and 2 per cent.

The major producers are Ontario, Quebec and British Columbia, which together account for 87 per cent of the production. Of particular note are the Noranda district in Quebec and the Sudbury district in Ontario. The smelter of the Noranda Mines, Ltd., in addition to processing the ore of the Noranda mine, also treats custom ores and concentrates from most of the copper mines in western Quebec, Ontario, and a mine in Manitoba. The International Nickel Company of Canada mines and processes the ores of the Sudbury district.

The "Timmins" Discovery

The discovery, in 1964, of a high grade zinc-silver-copper ore in a massive sulfur body eleven miles north of Timmins, Ontario, was an event of outstanding importance in the Canadian mineral industry. Tests have indicated 55 million tons of ore averaging 7.08 per cent zinc, 1.33 per cent copper, and 4.85 ounces of silver per ton. Production of zinc and copper concentrates began in late 1966 and output is expected to be about three million tons per year. It is estimated that this ore body will produce annually about 250,000 tons of zinc, 10,000 tons of lead, and 50,000 tons of copper. Recovery of silver and cadmium will also be part of the output of the mine.

South America

For more than 150 years the west coast of South America has been an important world source of copper. For many years, in the middle nineteenth century, Chile was the leading producer, but was eventually passed by the United States, the Copper Belt in Africa, and the U.S.S.R. Peru was also an early producer and still maintains a high rank among the producers of the world.

The copper industry of Chile consists of three sectors: American great mining companies, medium mining companies, and small copper mining companies. There are three large companies in the first category: Chile Exploration Company, Chuquicamata mine; Andes Copper Company, El Salvador mine; and Braden Copper Company, El Teniente mine. These three mining companies account for 90 per cent of the Chilean copper output. Chuquicamata, 160 rail miles northeast of the port of Antofagasta, is considered to be the largest economic copper deposit in the world. Large-scale, open-pit mining methods prevail, but underground mining will be introduced eventually. Reserves are estimated at from 600 million to 1000 million tons of ore containing 1.6 per cent copper.

The second largest Chilean producer is the underground El Teniente mine. It is at Sewell, in the province of O'Higgins, northeast of the city of Rancagua. The reserve is unofficially estimated at more than 350 million tons of ore containing 1.9 per cent copper.

The third of the three large mines is the El Salvador mine in the Province of Atacuma and east of the Port of Chanaral. This is also an underground mine. The average grade of ore is 1.6 per cent and the reserve is estimated at 375 million tons.

Copper in the Chilean Economy

The dominance of copper in the mineral industry of Chile has made its price and international demand of prime importance to the Chilean government. The three large producers pay direct taxes amounting to roughly one-fifth of the total tax receipts of the country and supply about 70 per cent of the foreign exchange needs. Additional millions enter the economy through the purchase by these companies of nearly half their operating requirements in the domestic market, plus special levies for road construction, irrigation, housing, and other public expenditures.

Peru

Peru entered the company of important copper producers when a new mine was opened in 1960. In that year the Southern Peru Copper Corporation started operations which resulted in tripling the output of the metal in that nation. This is an open pit mine with ore of 1.37 per cent copper content. Located at Toquepala, it ships its ore to the smelter at the port of Ilo. In the central Andean Range northeast of Lima the second largest copper producer, the Cerro Corporation, operates a smelter and five mines. The Northern Peru Mining Company, located east of Trujillo, is the third largest copper producer in Peru. These three companies account for more than 80 per cent of the nation's output.

Central Africa

The "Copper Belt" of Zambia and the copper districts of Katanga province in the Republic of the Congo together constitute the second largest world copper producing group of mining districts. Location of these districts is shown in the outline map of Africa and the inset map shows the location of mines and refineries.

Zambia

Among the three nations in the central African copper zone, Zambia is the leading producer and second only to the United States. The Congo follows with a substantial production while only modest production occurs in Rhodesia.

The copper industry of Zambia is situated in a relatively narrow strip of country known as the Copper Belt. The nation has six mines and three copper refineries owned by two mining groups. The estimated reserves of copper ore are 700 million tons, varying from 3 to 4.5 per cent copper content.

Zambia exports both blister copper and electrolytically refined copper; mainly to the United Kingdom, secondly to the nations of Western Europe. Considerable amounts also go to India, Japan, the United States, and the U.S.S.R.

Republic of the Congo

Copper produced in the Republic of the Congo comes from concessions of the now-nationalized Union Minière du Haut, in Katanga province. The important mines are concentrated in an area about 200

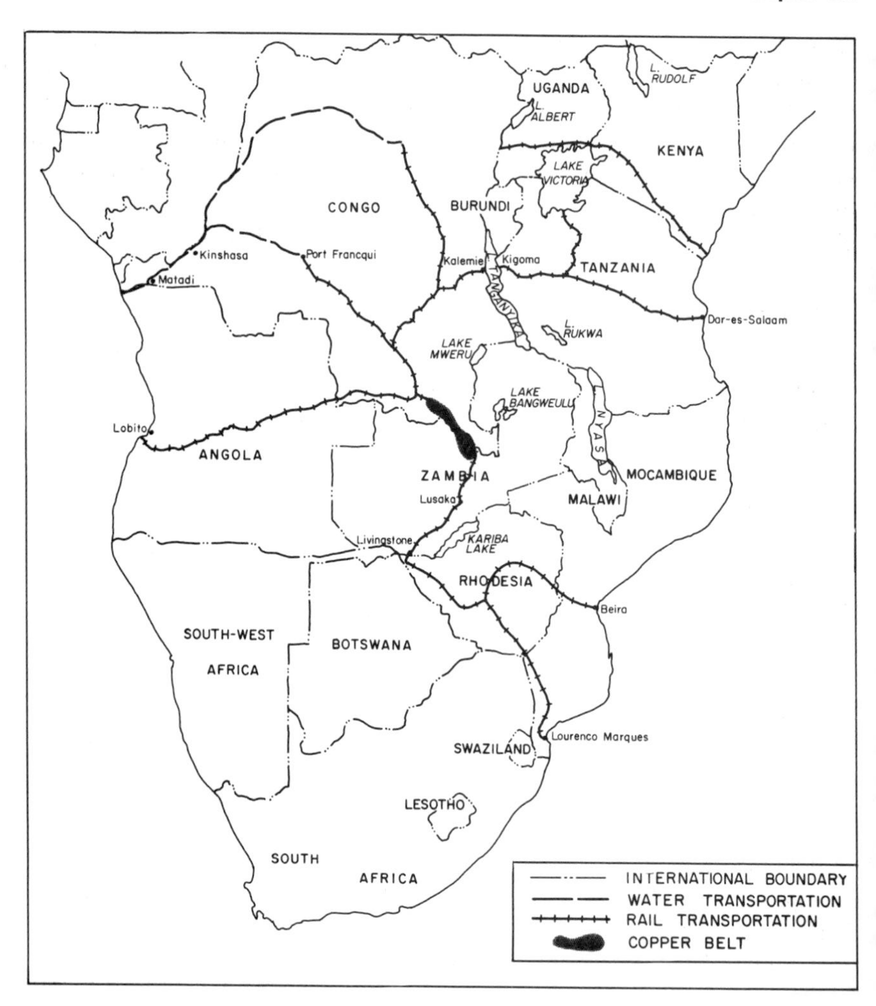

FIGURE 6.1 African Copper District

miles long, paralleling the Zambian border. There are three groups of mines localized around Kolwezi, Jadotville and Elizabethville. Markets for copper output are mainly Western European nations. Belgium is the largest buyer.

Transportation of copper from the land-locked producers in central Africa to world markets may be a critical factor. A study of the railway map shows three or possibly five outlets. To the east, the railways connect with the ports of Beira and Lourenço Marques. In this case ores from Katanga must pass through Zambia, Rhodesia, and Mozambique. To the west ores from Zambia must pass through the Republic of the

Congo and Angola to the port of Lobito. Possible alternative routes eastward are by rail to Dar es Salaam, involving a water crossing over Lake Tanganyika and Tanzania. Westward there is an alternative route to Port Francqui on the Kaisai River and thence by water transportation via the Congo to tidewater at Matadi. Political disturbances have, at times, hampered the flow of copper across neighboring nations and given rise to attempts to find alternate routes of shipment.

Southern Africa

The Republic of South Africa and Southwest Africa each produce about 1 per cent or less of the world's copper output. In Southwest Africa, copper production is of recent development.

copper in Europe

European nations (U.S.S.R. excepted) are insignificant in the production of copper. Altogether, the output is about 250,000 tons annually, or less than 5 per cent of the world's output. Industrial Europe, for her copper needs, draws upon Chile, Zambia, the Republic of the Congo, Peru and other less important producers. Mention should be made of Yugoslavia, Poland, East Germany and Finland as the more important among the European minor producers.

Asia

The reported production of copper in Asia is about 400,000 tons, among 11 countries. Among these, China, Japan, the Philippines and Turkey account for about 85 per cent. A Chinese source reports that discoveries of more than 3000 copper prospects have been made, but this is unconfirmed.

Australia

Australia ranks with Japan as a copper producer in the Orient, and is one of the two major copper producers in the Far East. Eight important mines, four smelters, and three refineries comprise the copper industry.

U.S.S.R.

Copper reserves and output in the U.S.S.R. are largely a matter of estimates. Principal copper deposits occur in five general areas: Kazakhstan, the Urals, Uzbekistan, Noril'sk, and Armenia. Kazakhstan accounts for more than half of the U.S.S.R. output of copper ore. The reported production in 1963 is given as 700,000 tons. Active prospecting and exploration has disclosed additional reserves and output has increased each year. The present seven-year plan (1958-1965) calls for an annual production of 1 million tons of copper by 1965.

copper: conclusion and summary

Almost fifty nations report the production of copper from a few hundred tons per year to more than one million. Three areas are outstanding in their contribution to the total output: the North American zone, the western slope of the Andes, and the Copper Belt of central Africa. Together these account for 80 per cent of the free world output. If the large estimated figures of the U.S.S.R. output are included, the four areas account for 82 per cent of the world total.

The possibilities of change in the status of a producing nation are always present. The activities of exploration geologists may uncover hitherto unknown deposits. Ore reserves increase as technological advances lower costs and permit the mining and processing of lower grade ore. And, because the grade of ore mined is also dependent on the market price of copper, a rise in price will automatically make available supplies of ore previously uneconomical to mine.

World copper reserves, as estimated in the year 1960 are shown in Table 6.1.

All quantities shown were considered to be measured or indicated ores that were minable under technologic and cost-price conditions prevailing in 1960. There is little doubt that potential copper resources are very large and, as old deposits become exhausted, new deposits must be found and developed.

Aluminum and Bauxite

The production of one pound of aluminum requires 4 pounds of crude bauxite, 0.4 pounds of carbon in an electrode, and 8 or 9 kilowatt hours of electric power. The location of aluminum reduction plants is a resultant of the geography of bauxite ores, the location of economical and adequate power supply, of materials assembling costs, and location of markets.

Processing of bauxite to aluminum involves two steps: (1) preparation of alumina (aluminum oxide) from the crude bauxite, (2) reduction of alumina to the free metal.

TABLE 6.1

World Copper Reserves

Country	Ore reserves copper content, thousand short tons
North America:	
Canada	8,400
Cuba	200
Haiti	75
Mexico	750
United States	32,500
Total	41,925
South America:	
Bolivia	55
Chile	46,000
Peru	12,500
Total	58,555
Europe:	
Austria	60
Bulgaria	300
Finland	750
East Germany	500
Ireland	280
Norway	500
Poland	11,400
Spain	4,500
Sweden	700
U.S.S.R.	35,000
Yugoslavia	2,750
Total	56,740
Asia:	
China	3,000
Cyprus	200
India	100
Israel	250
Japan	1,200
Philippines	1,000
Turkey	580
Total	6,330
Africa:	
Angola	40
Republic of the Congo	20,000
Northern Rhodesia	25,000
Southern Rhodesia	475
Kenya	20
Mauritania	460
Southwest Africa	525
Uganda	210
Republic of South Africa	900
Total	47,630
Oceania: Australia	1,200
GRAND TOTAL	212,000

the geographic structure of the aluminum industry

The geographic structure of the aluminum industry is conditioned by the fact that the raw materials are located primarily in the tropics, while the aluminum reduction plants tend to be located near sources of low cost electric power, in or near the world's major industrial districts. There are some exceptions to this generalization which will be noted later.

Caribbean-North American Structure

The raw material base for aluminum production in the United States and Canada is the group of bauxite deposits in Jamaica, Guyana, Surinam, and small additions from Haiti and the Dominican Republic. The United States, from its domestic sources in Arkansas, contributes about 14 per cent of the total crude bauxite uesd by the two nations. Among these sources of bauxite the island of Jamaica is the world's foremost producer. The relative position of the Caribbean bauxite producers is indicated by output in 1966 as shown in Table 6.2.

TABLE 6.2

World Bauxite Output

Country	Thousand long tons production
Jamaica	9,000
Surinam	5,200
Guyana	2,800
Dominican Republic	942
Haiti	325
Total	18,267

All but a small fraction of the crude bauxite exported from these countries is shipped to calcining plants in the United States and Canada. These plants are located in Alabama, Texas, Louisiana, and Arkansas: states in which supplies of natural gas are abundant and low-cost. Shipments to Canada are destined to Arvida, Quebec, next to the aluminum reduction plant.

In addition to exporting crude bauxite, Jamaica and Guyana also have plants for the calcining of raw bauxite to alumina. The output of these plants is destined mainly to Norway and Canada.

aluminum reduction plants

The United States and Canada account for about 60 per cent of the free world's aluminum output. The United States has about twenty-four plants for aluminum reduction and Canada has six. In Canada, all reduction plants are operated by hydroelectric power plants located at Arvida, Shawinigan, Isle Maligne, Baie Comeau, and Beauharnois, all in Quebec, and Kitimat in British Columbia.

Plants in the United States are located at Massena, New York adjacent to hydroelectric power plants on the St. Lawrence River, and at various hydroelectric power plants in Tennessee, North Carolina, Alabama, and Washington State. Power plants for aluminum reduction works in Louisiana and Texas operate on natural gas.

the European bauxite-aluminum pattern

The aluminum manufacturing industry of Europe (exclusive of U.S.S.R.) is practically self-sufficient with respect to bauxite supply. There are minor contributions from outside Europe, mainly from Guyana and the Republic of Guinea. Four European nations are producers of bauxite. In order of importance they are France, Hungary, Greece, and Yugoslavia. France ranks fifth among world producers. Domestic production is adequate for the aluminum industry and provides a surplus for export. Visible and indicated reserves were estimated to total 30 million tons of which 80 per cent is in the Department of Var.

The central Hungarian mountains are the principal source of bauxite although a deposit of more limited size has been located in the western part of the country. The reserves are estimated at between 200 million and 380 million long tons.

Greek bauxite deposits are located mainly south of Mt. Parnassus but are found also on the island of Euboea. Reserves are estimated at 12 million tons proven plus 50-60 million tons of possible ore. In Yugoslavia, the bulk of the bauxite reserves are in deposits near the Adriatic Coast. A recent discovery near Zadar in Dalmatia adds 38 million tons to the nation's previously measured 150-million ton reserve.

Alumina processing plants are located in France, West Germany, Italy, Yugoslavia, and in smaller capacities in Norway and Sweden.

Australia

Australia has one of the world's richest bauxite resources with a reserve estimated to exceed 3 billion tons. Estimates put the known deposits in northern Australia alone, chiefly at Weipa on the remote northern tip of Cape York Peninsula, at more than 3 billion tons, of which about 2 billion would be of metallurgical grade. The grade averages 46 to 52 per cent Al_2O_3. On the Gove Peninsula flanking the Gulf of Carpentaria on the west, in Northern Territory, is another large deposit estimated to contain more than 100 million tons of bauxite.

A third significant deposit of bauxite in the Darling Range, near Perth, in western Australia, extends over 200 miles in length. This area has been estimated to contain 80 million long tons, average 30 to 45 per cent Al_2O_3. The potential of extensive deposits at widely separate locations has stimulated the development of a fully integrated aluminum industry. Ores from the deposits at Weipa are shipped to Bell Bay, Tasmania, for processing to alumina. Furthermore, Comalco, operator of the Weipa mines, is planning a reduction plant on New Zealand's South Island, where ample hydroelectric power is available.

In the meantime, Alcoa, operator of the bauxite deposits in the Darling Ranges of southwestern western Australia, is building a plant at Kwinana for the processing of bauxite to alumina. This will be shipped to Port Henry, near Geelong, Victoria, where a reduction and fabricating aluminum plant has been established. Electric power is generated from local coal deposits.

Lead

Lead is a "precious metal" if we measure a metal's worth by the number of its uses and its indispensability in goods that add to human comfort and welfare in our machine economy. As a metal, an alloying agent, an ingredient of manufactured goods, an agent in industrial operations, and in chemical compounds, lead's usefulness is as wide as the field of industry itself. In the home lead is in paint, pottery, glassware, plumbing, and musical instruments; in the office it is used in typewriters and calculating machines; it is in the various vehicles of transportation, automobile, airplane and locomotive; in building-trade materials, printing industry equipment, the sportsman's rifle, the chemical laboratory.

The properties of lead make it unsuitable for structural purposes. Its tensile strength, as ordinarily determined, is 2600 to 3300 pounds per square inch; lower than that of most other metals. Unlike many other metals, its tensile strength is not increased to any appreciable extent by alloying.

Chemically, lead's useful properties surpass those of other common metals. Under ordinary conditions of atmospheric corrosion, the life of lead may be measured in centuries. Because lead is so chemically inert, it is used for roofing, water pipes, and leading of glass windows. It is so resistant to corrosion that it is employed for containers and equipment in manufacturing and handling sulfuric acid.

The wide variety of uses for this metal fall provisionally into three groups: (1) uses of the pure metal, (2) uses in alloyed form, and (3) uses in chemical compounds.

the ores of lead and zinc

Lead and zinc ores are frequently associated. With but few exceptions, ores that are mined for their lead content generally contain commercial quantities of zinc, and the reverse is equally true. The principal minerals in lead and zinc ores are galena (lead sulfide) with a lead content of 86.6 per cent and sphalerite (zinc sulfide) with a zinc content of 67 per cent. Other lead minerals of lesser importance are cerussite (lead carbonate) and anglesite (lead sulfate), and for zince, smithsonite (zinc carbonate) and hemimorphite (zinc silicate).

Ores of lead and zinc frequently also contain minor quantities of copper, silver and gold. Cadmium is associated with zinc ore as a by-product, which is the only source of this metal.

world lead resources

Lead is produced in every continent and nearly 50 nations among these six continents. Reported world lead reserves are given at 51 million net tons (lead content) distributed among the continents as shown in the accompanying Table 6.3.

The lead reserves given in Table 6.3 include only lead in ores that have been inventoried and were economic at the time of inventory. These reserves include lead in measured and indicated ores, but make no allowance for inferred and undiscovered ores.

lead in North America

The nations of Canada, the United States, and Mexico contain one-third of the world's known reserves of lead. Canada ranks first among

TABLE 6.3

Reported Lead Reserves

Continent	Lead Content	Per cent of Total
North America	16,368,000	32.2
South America	2,500,000	5.0
Europe, Eastern	4,600,000	9.1
Europe, Western	9,100,000	18.0
Africa	3,500,000	7.0
Asia	2,000,000	3.9
Australia	12,500,000	24.7
Total	50,818,000	100.0

these three. The principal producer is the Sullivan mine at Kimberly, British Columbia. This mine alone accounts for 60 per cent of Canada's lead output and together with three other mines makes up nearly 80 per cent of the nation's output. In eastern Canada, the Buchans mine in Newfoundland is second to British Columbia mines. Together these two provinces account for 90 per cent of Canada's output. Other mines are located in Manitoba, Ontario, Quebec, New Brunswick and Nova Scotia.

The United States

Estimated lead reserves in the United States are lower than Canada although output is larger. Missouri ranks first among the states in lead production and is one of the leading lead producing districts in the world. The deposits lie in a belt over 60 miles long and 20 miles wide in parts of St. Francois, Iron, Washington, and Madison counties. Recent discoveries on the western extension of southeast Missouri's lead belt have enhanced the state's premier position in the domestic lead industry. There is a small output of lead in the tri-state district comprising parts of Missouri, Kansas, and Oklahoma.

In the western states, the Coeur d' Alene district in Idaho ranks next to Missouri as a producer. The district is also a first ranking silver producer, a major zinc producer, and a producer of significant quantities of copper, antimony, and gold. The district lies on the western slope of the Coeur d' Alene Mountains in Shoshone County. In Utah the lead producing district lies within a radius of 70 miles east, west and south of Salt Lake City. In Colorado lead production centers mainly in two districts around Leadville and in the southwestern part of the state.

The above four states account for 90 per cent of the nation's lead output. Other producing states are Arizona, California, Illinois, Montana, New Mexico, New York, Virginia, Washington, and Wisconsin.

In Mexico there are many small deposits which in the aggregate contribute to the national lead supply. However, the principal source of the metal comes from a few mining districts in southern Chihuahua state and to the southeast in northern Zacatecas and San Luís Potosí states. Owing to the nature of ore occurrence, these districts also contain most of the country's zinc and silver reserves.

lead in Europe

Ten nations in Europe each produce more than 10,000 tons of the metal. Production is concentrated in Yugoslavia, Sweden, Spain, West Germany, Poland, and Italy. Yugoslavia is exceptionally rich in lead-zinc deposits. The most productive district is in southern Serbia and northern Macedonia. It is the largest lead producing nation in Europe.

Bulgaria is a close second to Yugoslavia as a lead producer. The ores also contain zinc, copper, silver, and gold.

In West Germany, among the many lead bearing deposits, three are outstanding, the largest of which is in the Eifel district west of the Rhine. Ore is low in grade but the reserves are large, about 300 million tons. These are estimated to represent about one-third of the total Western European reserves.

In Italy, the zinc-lead mineral deposits àre grouped in the southwestern part of the island of Sardinia. The deposits occurring in north Italy are also important.

The major deposits in Poland are concentrated in central Silesia in the vicinity of Katowice. Reserves were estimated at 20 million tons but the widespread occurrence of mineralization indicates that the potential ore tonnages are much greater than the reported measured reserves.

In the southern part of Spain are two mountain ranges that rank among the great lead provinces of the world. The northern of these is the Sierra Morena Range. The mines yield silver as a by-product of lead. Bordering the southeast coast is the Sierra Nevada Range, the second Spanish lead province. Ores in this range also contain zinc.

Nations in Europe producing less than 1 per cent of the continent's output are Austria, Finland, East Germany, and Norway.

Little specific information can be given about the lead and zinc deposits of the Soviet Union. Three regions apparently contain the major reserves of lead and zinc. The most important are in Turkestan, especially at the western end of the Altai Mountains of eastern Kazakhstan. The deposit at Leninogorsk ranks among the world's largest. Another important region of lead deposits is that northeast of Alma-Ata in southern Kazakhstan. The North Caucasus contain the second most significant region, the Sadon deposits near Misur, and the Far East Tetyukhe deposits rank third.

other areas

In Asia the principal lead producers are China, Japan and North Korea. In China the producing districts have been in Yunnan and Hunan provinces and in Manchuria. Recent discoveries are reported in Tsinghai, Szechwan, Kansu, Hupeh, Kwangsi, Kwangtung and Sinkiang provinces.

In Africa the two major producers are Morocco and Southwest Africa. The larger of the two major ore deposits is located twenty-five miles south of Oujda on the Algerian border. The measured reserve is estimated at 15 million tons and the indicated and presently submarginal reserve is some large multiple of the measured reserve figure. A second important reserve is in central Morocco south of the Middle Atlas Range.

Other lead producers of minor significance in Africa are Algeria, the Congo, Tunisia, and Zambia.

South America

Seventy per cent of lead output in South America is in Peru. This nation ranks sixth among the lead producers of the world. The Cerro de Pasco deposit outranks all others in the nation. The Peruvian ores are complex with zinc, lead, copper and silver present together with minor values in gold and bismuth. In addition to the Cerro deposit, several additional deposits contribute to the nation's large output.

Australia

Australia is the first ranking nation in the world in lead output. The ores are complex, containing lead, zinc, and silver. The principal producing areas are the Broken Hill district, New South Wales, the Mt. Isa district, Queensland, and the Reed-Rosebery district in Tasmania.

international trade in lead

The United States and the nations of Western Europe are the dominant lead using areas of the world. Lead mined in the industrial areas of the world does not enter international trade, but is consumed in the country of origin. Among these countries are the United States, the U.S.S.R., West Germany, France, Italy, and Japan. Several Western European nations having no indigenous lead must import their total requirements. Examples are Belgium, Denmark, the Netherlands, and Switzerland. The United Kingdom, a large lead consuming nation, imports practically all of the lead it consumes.

Mexico, Canada, Peru, Australia, Yugoslavia, Southwest Africa, Algeria, and Morocco are countries having large lead mine production but relatively small internal need. The products of these countries enter international trade.

A few nations of the world, Argentina, Italy, and the U.S.S.R., are self-sufficient in lead but do not produce exportable surpluses.

the influence of scrap

The growth in reclamation of lead from scrap has a significant effect upon the total lead supply. In the United States the annual supply of lead from recovered sources exceeds the supply of primary lead from both domestic and imported sources. It is estimated that about 50 per cent of the lead put into use is ultimately recovered as scrap. The chief source of lead scrap is automobile storage batteries. Estimated ultimate recovery of the lead content of automobile storage batteries is 80 per cent. Additional sources of recoverable lead scrap include cable sheathing, plumbing, pipes, sheets, solder, type metal, leaded brasses, and bronzes.

Zinc

Zinc is closely associated with lead in ore bodies and many a producing mine yields both minerals. In use, however, zinc occupies an entirely different area in its industrial applications than does lead. The four major uses of zinc are die casting, galvanizing, brass, and rolled products. The manufacture of zinc die casting in the United States is closely related to the automobile manufacturing industry. It is the most important use of zinc in the United States and second in importance in Europe and Japan. In the die casting processes, castings are produced in quantity by forcing molten zinc alloy into steel dies at high pressures and temperatures. Die casting permits production of intricate parts within close limits of accuracy. Zinc die castings are used in automobile hardware, electrical appliances, business machines, tools, building hardware, and toys.

The use of zinc in galvanizing ranks second in the United States and Western Europe and first in Japan. Zinc coating or galvanizing is applied to a great tonnage of steel products and is the most economical means of corrosion protection available. When exposed to the atmosphere, a coating of relatively insoluble zinc carbonate forms on the surface of the zinc metal which inhibits further corrosion. The major application of zinc coating on steel products include roofing and siding sheets, wire and wire products for outside exposure, articles fabricated from sheet steel, such as range boilers, pails, cans and tanks, hardware for outdoor use, pipe and conduit, and exposed structural steel. Nails are galvanized, not only to extend the life of the nail but also to prevent rotting of wood or rusting of galvanized sheet.

Rolled zinc is not important in the United States but prevails in Europe where rolled zinc products are widely used in the construction industry. Major outlets in the United States at present include battery cans, Mason jar tops, photo engraving plates, and similar minor applications.

Minor uses of zinc are zinc oxide and zinc dust. The oxide is used in compounding rubber and in making paint, ceramic materials, textiles, floor coverings, and paper coating. The use of zinc oxide in rubber manufacture appears to be increasing. Zinc dust is used in making zinc salts and compounds, to purify fats, to manufacture dyes, and to precipitate gold and silver from cyanide solutions. The more industrially important compounds of zinc are zinc chloride, zinc sulfate, and lithopone, a mixture of barium sulfate and zinc sulfide for paint manufacture.

zinc resources

Zinc is produced in every continent and, in varying quantities, in about sixty nations. The ores of zinc are widely distributed. Reserves, measured and indicated as of 1965, total 85 million tons. Their distribution is shown in Table 6.4.
Among the nations Canada outranks all others in reserves and output, followed by the United States and Australia.

Zinc production in the United States comes from many districts which are graduated in annual output so that no sharp break separates the major from the minors. Of the twenty-five leading mines which yield three-fourths of the zinc output, seven are in Tennessee; three each in Idaho and New Mexico; two each in Colorado and New York;

TABLE 6.4

World Zinc Reserves—Measured and Indicated

World Zinc Reserves—Measured and Indicated

	Thousand Tons
United States	12,000
Australia	5,000
Canada	19,000
Mexico	4,000
Other Free World	26,000
Communist Countries (except Yugoslavia)	17,000
WORLD TOTAL	83,000

and one each in New Jersey, Pennsylvania, Virginia, Montana, Washington, Utah, Arizona, and Wisconsin. Tennessee maintains its lead as a producer among the twenty-four producing states and together with New York, Idaho, and Colorado, accounts for half of the total output. The United States is not self-sufficient in domestic zinc supplies but imports almost half of its needs, principally from Canada, Mexico and Peru, with minor quantities from other foreign producers.

Canada is the world's leading zinc producer. Mines in British Columbia and in the Flin Flon district on the Manitoba-Saskatchewan border account for more than half of the output. Quebec, Ontario and Newfoundland also make important contributions. Canada exports zinc concentrates and metal to the United States, United Kingdom, and Belgium-Luxembourg.

Mexico is the third large producer of zinc in North America, and together the three nations produce one-third of the world's zinc output. The principal zinc mines of Mexico are located in the states of Chihuahua and Zacatecas and are associated with lead mines.

In South America Peru is the dominant zinc producer. Among four nations contributing to zinc output, Peru accounts for 90 per cent. The other three producers are Argentina, Chile, and Colombia.

European nations (exclusive of the U.S.S.R.) in the aggregate produce slightly more zinc than Canada. Poland is the leading producer followed by Italy, West Germany, Spain, Bulgaria, Sweden, and Finland. The remaining producers are Austria, France, East Germany,

Greece, Norway, Hungary, and Portugal. The lead-zinc resources of Germany and Poland are somewhat difficult to differentiate, since with the changes in national boundaries, accrediting of production has changed from one country to another. The major deposits are in Silesia and the important lead-zinc deposits are in Upper Silesia which is now entirely in Poland.

Zinc is one of the more important mineral products of Italy. In addition to domestic processing of the ore, shipments are also made to France, Belgium-Luxembourg, and Austria.

The nations of Western Europe, as a group, are not self-sufficient in zinc supplies. While there is a considerable interchange among them in ores, concentrates, zinc slabs, and finished products, there is, in addition to these interchanges, a considerable import from Canada, Peru, Iran, Algeria, Morocco, the Congo, Southwest Africa and Zambia. In the U.S.S.R. lead-zinc deposits occur in the Urals, in the Krasnoyarsk region, in Altai, Kazakhstan and Azerbaijan.

Australia

The zinc and nearly all the lead produced in Australia is mined in ores that contain varying quantities of gold, silver, copper, cadmium, manganese, and other elements. Virtually all production has been from the four localities of Broken Hill, and Captain's Flat in New South Wales, Mt. Isa, in Queensland, and Reed-Rosebery, in Tasmania.

Chapter 7

Plant Foods

Although multitudes of different species of plants grow upon many kinds of soil, some twenty elements are known to be essential to plant growth. Four of these elements are derived from water and air, and the others come from the soil. Although a deficiency may occur with respect to any or several of them, those most likely to be lacking in the soil in adequate proportions are *calcium, phosphorus, potassium* and *nitrogen.* Calcium deficiency is probably the most widespread but will not be considered here because enormous quantities of limestone are available in nearly all the agricultural areas of the world.

Geographic Aspects of Fertilizer Supply

nitrogen

It may seem curious that plants should suffer for want of nitrogen when the earth's atmosphere, enveloping all plant life, is a gaseous blanket of which 80 per cent is nitrogen. The difficulty lies in the fact that the nitrogen in the air is inert and in a form not suitable for absorption by the tiny rootlets of growing plants. Before the plant can use nitrogen as a nutrient, it must be combined with some other element or elements to form a soluble salt.

The present supply of soil nitrogen is merely an accumulation of air nitrogen fixed in the soil over a long period of years. The gateway through which the nitrogen of the air must pass into the soil is a narrow one indeed. Very likely the first entry is through a group of microscopic plants, the nitrogen-fixing bacteria, which have the power to assimilate free nitrogen and combine it into a form in which it is available to plants. Certain other types of bacteria, the symbiotic bacteria, living in close relationship to plants of the legume family, also absorb and synthesize free nitrogen.

sources of commercial nitrogen

There are three significant sources of nitrogen compounds used mainly for plant nutrients: (1) natural deposits of nitrate salts, (2) ammonia synthesis, and (3) by-product nitrogen compounds obtained mainly as a by-product of the coking industry.

natural nitrates

The only commercially important nitrate deposits in the world are in Chile, in an area 10 to 50 miles wide and 450 miles long between the Coast Range and the Andes Mountains in northern Chile. The nitrate-bearing ores contain 5 to 30 per cent sodium nitrate and a smaller quantity of potassium nitrate. Exploitation of nitrates began in the middle of the nineteenth century, and for some time thereafter Chile was the principal world source of fixed nitrogen. This continued until a process was developed to make synthetic compounds, using nitrogen from the air. Although nitrates from Chile now account for about 6 per cent of the world fixed nitrogen output, the total demand for nitrogen has so increased that the Chilean output is not diminishing. The decline in Chile's share of the nitrogen market has been in percentage, not in tonnage.

synthetic nitrogen

Nitrogen fixation means combining nitrogen with other elements to make soluble compounds such as anhydrous ammonia (NH_3), urea, ammonium sulfate, ammonium nitrate, or ammonium phosphate. This nitrogen is referred to as atmospheric nitrogen. This is, by far, the most important source of fixed nitrogen. The initial process is the production of anhydrous ammonia by combining hydrogen and nitrogen under high temperature and pressure in the presence of a catalyst. This compound may be injected directly into the soil or converted into other fertilizer materials. Hydrogen, the more costly of the two raw materials, is obtained mainly from natural gas, although it is also obtainable by blowing steam against red-hot coke or by the electrolysis of water.

While the practice of applying anhydrous ammonia directly to the soil is becoming more widespread, much of the agricultural ammonia is still converted into derivatives, such as ammonium nitrate or urea. These have advantages, because of ease of transportation, storage, and application.

In the production of nitrogen-containing phosphate fertilizers, several material producing companies have a direct interest, and, because of this interest, have themselves become fertilizer producers. Among these are the producers of natural gas, the raw material for the production of hydrogen. Sulfur producing companies have also become interested in phosphate fertilizer production as a means of marketing sulfuric acid in rock phosphate treatment. Steel companies also have shown an interest as a means of disposal of their by-product ammonia from the coke plant.

phosphates

Phosphate rock does not have a definite chemical composition. It may contain one or more phosphate minerals; one is usually calcium phosphate. The phosphorus content of naturally occurring phosphate minerals is not readily available to plants so that these minerals are usually treated to convert the phosphate content to a form readily available to plants. The principal forms of commercial phosphate fertilizers are

1. Superphosphate (16-20% P_2O_5[1] equiv.). Normal superphosphate is the most important source of fertilizer phosphorus but is diminishing in favor of more concentrated forms.
2. Triple superphosphate (46-48% P_2O_5 equiv.). This is made by treating ground phosphate rock with phosphoric acid. Plants for the manufacture of TSP are usually located at the mine to take advantage of shipping a concentrated product.
3. Diammonium phosphate. This is prepared by combining anhydrous ammonia (NH_3) with phosphoric acid. The product contains two plant fertilizers at a ratio of units (NPK) of about 18-48-0. Potassium chloride can be added at the mixing stage to make a "complete" fertilizer.

distribution of phosphates

Deposits of phosphate rock occur in many countries, but only a few have deposits or production in significant quantities. The major areas,

[1]The unit of value of a phosphate fertilizer is phosphorus pentoxide (P_2O_5). The value of any phosphate fertilizer is measured by the number of P_2O_5 units present in it.

in descending order of importance are the United States; the U.S.S.R.; North Africa, in Morocco, Tunisia, United Arab Republic; in the rest of Africa, Togo, Republic of South Africa, and Senegal; Christmas Island in the Indian Ocean; and in Oceania, on Makatea, Nauru, and Ocean Islands.

the United States

The United States, with one-third of the world's known reserves, leads in world output and export. Phosphate production and reserves are located in Florida, Tennessee, North Carolina, and the western states of Idaho, Montana, Wyoming, and Utah. Interest in the eastern deposits is active because these deposits are closer to the large fertilizer consuming areas. This is important because phosphate is a high bulk, low value commodity and freight rates are a large factor in competition among producers.

Florida

The important phosphate district in Florida is the alluvial pebble deposit in Polk and Hillsborough Counties, adjacent to Tampa Bay. In 1965, the field accounted for 75 per cent of the phosphate production in the United States. Polk County is the leading producer and, together with sand and gravel output, accounted for half of the value of the entire state's mineral output.

Development and output of phosphate fertilizers has been rapid since 1950. During the ensuing years there was also a change in the pattern of the industry from mining to mining and manufacturing. Chemical plants for making phosphoric acid, superphosphate, triple superphosphate, diammonium phosphate, and other concentrated phosphates for fertilizers sprang up in association with the mining plants. The result was that chemical processes upgraded the product and increased the range of market area and the reserves of minable rock by lowering the cut-off grade.

In 1965, another phosphate field was opened in northern Florida at White Springs in Hamilton County. A mine and ore dressing plant, a chemical plant manufacturing concentrated phosphate fertilizers, and a port loading facility at Jacksonville have been constructed.

Tennessee

Phosphate mining in Tennessee began shortly after the beginning of the industry in Florida, but the high grade ore has mostly been mined out. In 1955, output in the state was surpassed by that of the western states. The grade of ore is too low to be used for the manufacture of phosphoric acid. As a result most of the rock is used for electric furnace feed in the manufacture of elemental phosphorus. Tennessee has limited reserves of ore and great expansion in this field is not likely.

North Carolina

North Carolina began production on April 1, 1966, from phosphate deposits discovered a few years previously. Preliminary figures indicate that the North Carolina deposits, in Beaufort County on the Pamlico River, contain some 2 billion tons of phosphate rock. The phosphate reserves cover an area of some 700 square miles. The ore body has a thickness ranging up to 120 feet with the average probably 40 or 50 feet.[2]

Western Phosphate Deposits

The western phosphate deposits are located in Idaho, Montana, Wyoming, and Utah. The principal production is in Idaho and Montana, although mining operations have also begun near Vernal, Utah.

The United States exports nearly one-third of its phosphate rock production. European nations constitute the largest importing area followed by Japan. Other nations importing substantial quantities are Canada, Mexico, Brazil, Australia, and New Zealand.

North African phosphate deposits

The leading phosphate producer in Africa is Morocco, which accounts for two-thirds of that continent's output. Tunisia and the United Arab Republic are also producers. Morocco and Tunisia play an important role in the agricultural economy of Europe and Asia and, to a smaller degree, in Oceania. Of an export total of 13.5 million tons of phosphate rock in 1964, a little more than 11 million tons was shipped to Europe, 1.5 million tons to Asia, and the remainder to North America.

South America and Africa

France, West Germany, Belgium, United Kingdom, Spain, the Netherlands, and Italy were the principal recipients although a total of 22 countries participated. In addition to Morocco and Tunisia, Senegal and Togo also made small contributions.

---

[2]*New York Times,* March 15, 1964.

U.S.S.R.

The Soviets report a proved reserve of 3 billion tons of phosphate ores equally divided between the apatite deposits in the Khibiny District of the Kola Peninsula in the extreme northwest, the phosphate rocks in the Karatan Basin of Kazakhstan, and low grade concretionary ores in a larger number of relatively small deposits. Currently exploitable ores are not found east of the Urals.

other producers

In Oceania, Nauru, Maketea, and Ocean islands are the principal producers, but small in comparison with major producers. In Asia small production is reported in several nations, notably Christmas Island and North Vietnam.

Potash

Potash is widely distributed in nature, yet only a few localities have economic resources of this group of mineral salts. The expression "potash" is commonly applied to the primary potassium-bearing materials; more specifically, it refers to their content of potassium oxide (K_2O) equivalent, a term used to permit comparison among the several commercial potassium salts.

The common and most useful potassium-bearing minerals are shown in Table 7.1.

TABLE 7.1

Common Potassium-bearing Minerals

Mineral	Formula	Percentages K_2O equivalent
Sylvite	KCl	63.3
Carnallite	$KCl.MgCl_2.6H_2O$	17.0
Langbeinite	$K_2SO_4.MgSO_4$	22.0
Kainite	$KCl.MgSO_4.3H_2O$	18.9
Nitre	KNO_3	46.5

Minerals valued for their potassium content occur almost entirely as bedded evaporite deposits associated with salt or as natural brines (as in the Dead Sea) where soluble salts are being concentrated by high rates of evaporation. The main sources of potash are evaporites that, after deposition, have been buried by overlying sediments and thus protected from solution by surface water. Major deposits of potash have been found in East and West Germany, Canada, the United States, France, and the U.S.S.R.

the United States

The potash industry in the United States began in 1916 when muriate of potash was first obtained from the brines of Searles Lake in California. The brines of the Salduro marshes at Wendover, Utah provided another source.

The major source of potash in the United States has been the Carlsbad, New Mexico deposits which were first mined in 1931. These are underground deposits largely of sylvanite at 800- to 1300-foot depths. The Carlsbad potash mines have become the most important source of the fertilizer salts in the United States. More than 90 per cent of the potash salts come from the Carlsbad mines, but the beginning of production of an extensive salt bed in Utah will ultimately change this proportion. Potash fertilizers are shipped to all the fifty states; the agricultural states of the Mississippi and Ohio valleys take nearly 50 per cent of the output. About one-fifth of the production is exported, the largest single importer being Japan. Canada exports potash salts to the United States.

In Utah production from a large underground deposit near Moab, at a 3000-3300-foot depth began in 1965.

Canada

Large potash reserves were discovered in Canada in 1943, primarily in the province of Saskatchewan near Esterhazy. The formation underlies the entire width of Saskatchewan and extends both into Manitoba and Alberta. The full extent of these deposits is not known, but they are estimated to be at least 6.5 billion tons. As much as 17,500 million tons has been indicated.[3] The Canadian deposits consist of sylvanite with a somewhat higher K_2O content than is found in Carlsbad or Moab. Although the deposits are from 3000 to 6000 feet deep, their size and K_2O content make them attractive for commercial exploitation.

[3]U.S. Bureau of Mines, *Commodity Data Summaries*, 1966, p. 73.

The room and pillar method of mining is used in Saskatchewan generally, but also in operation is a solution mining method. The principle of solution mining is to pump hot solution down pipes to the bed, dissolve out the potassium salts, and return the brine through other pipes to the surface for refining. Salts occurring at 5000 to 6000 feet can be reached by this method.

Federal Republic of Germany

Germany discovered deposits of water-soluble potash near Stassfurt about the middle of the nineteenth century. Germany's extensive deposits lie in a well-defined subterranean basin, embracing some 24,000 square miles, which runs southeastward from Hanover province in the northwest through Saxony and Thuringia. Another potash deposit, apparently separate from the main basin and believed to be continuous with deposits in Alsace-Lorraine, is in Baden province. The states of Niedersachsen and Hesse produce about 95 per cent of the output and the small remainder is produced in Baden-Württenberg.

In East Germany potash is the principal nonmetallic product. More than half of the total output comes from Erfurt where reserves are extensive. Much of the output is exported.

France ranks immediately below the United States, West and East Germany, as a producer of potash salts. Discovery of potash near Wittelsheim in the Alsace region of France was made in 1904. Alsatian reserves are less extensive than German, but they are richer, occur in more regular beds, and consist of simpler mixtures, which makes it easier to mine and refine the salts.

France exports crude potash salts and potassic fertilizers to Belgium-Luxembourg, the Netherlands, the United Kingdom, Switzerland, Ireland, Italy, Japan, and the United States.

Spain. Potash deposits in Spain are extensive and reserve estimates are upwards of 500 million tons containing 15 per cent K_2O. The bulk of production comes from Barcelona Province where deposits were first discovered in 1912. Only recently has production begun in Navarra Province where deposits were discovered in 1950.

Italy. Production of potash began in Italy in 1957 and since then has made rapid progress. The producing mines are located in the Caltanisseta and Enna areas of Sicily.

Israel. Potash salts are recovered from the Dead Sea by solar evaporation.

Ethiopia. Potash deposits occur near Dallol in the northern part of the Danakil Depression inland from the Red Sea. They are estimated at upwards of 50 million metric tons of sylvite in a sedimentary zone about three meters thick. Development of these deposits would involve construction of a treatment plant, a 100-kilometer standard-guage railway from the plant to the Red Sea, and a deepwater port at Ras Andarge.

Sulfur

Sulfur stands next to iron as one of the most widely used minerals of modern industry. Although sulfur is mined in much smaller quantities than iron its uses are so varied and so fundamental that it is an indispensable element in many industrial operations. Large tonnages of sulfur go into the manufacture of chemicals, including explosives and military materials, fertilizers, insecticides, wood pulp and paper, dyes and coal tar products, rubber, paint and varnish, and food products.

About 80 per cent of sulfur from all sources is used in the manufacture of sulfuric acid. Although the acid is essential in many manufacturing processes, the largest quantity is used in the treatment of rock phosphate for the production of commercial fertilizers. The rapid growth in demand for fertilizer materials has also affected the demand for sulfur with the result that the industry has expanded recently and further growth is anticipated.

Present and potential sources of sulfur of varying degrees of practicality are as follows:

1. Native sulfur in salt domes, principally in the Texas and Louisiana Gulf Coast and in Mexico.
2. Hydrogen sulfide in natural gas.
3. Sulfides of nonferrous metals – lead, zinc, copper – obtained from smelter gases.
4. Hydrogen sulfide from oil refinery operations.
5. Pyrites.
6. Sulfur from coal
   a. Coal brasses (iron pyrite) separated from coal at cleaning plants.
   b. Hydrogen sulfide from by-product coke oven gases.
   c. Sulfur dioxide from stack gases of coal-burning power plants.
7. Gypsum and anhydrite.
8. Low grade sulfur deposits.
9. Athabasca tar sands.

sulfur in the United States and Mexico

Frasch sulfur. Native sulfur occurs in several nations but the most important and most widely known are the salt dome deposits on the

Gulf coasts of Louisiana and Texas and in Mexico. Sulfur in these salt domes is produced by a unique system of mining known as the Frasch process. In this method the mining company sinks a pipe into the sulfur bearing rocks in the salt dome and forces hot water in under pressure. The hot water, escaping through perforations in the pipe, melts the sulfur. Compressed air forces the molten sulfur upward through another pipe into basins where it is allowed to solidify. Of the 230 or more salt domes discovered in Louisiana and Texas, only 21 have been productive and 8 are exhausted. The United States and Mexico are the only nations producing sulfur by the Frasch method and together they produce between 30 and 35 per cent of the free world's sulfur output.

Sulfur from Sour Gas

"Sour gas" is a term applied to natural gas in which hydrogen sulfide is present. Obviously gas contaminated with this ingredient is unsuitable for use as a fuel until the sulfide is removed. The separation is, however, not an unrecompensed cost, since hydrogen sulfide is a raw material for the production of elemental sulfur or of useful sulfur compounds. Recovery of elemental sulfur from sour gas is the most significant fact in the changing sulfur picture.

By-product sulfur from sour gas is being recovered in Arkansas, Texas, New Mexico, and Wyoming. Production of sulfur recovered from sour natural gas and refinery gases now exceeds 1 million tons.

In addition to by-product sulfur from gases, sulfur is also produced through the processing of pyrites, notably in Pennsylvania, Colorado, Arizona, and South Carolina.

Copper and zinc plants in California, Louisiana, New Jersey, Pennsylvania and Tennessee produce sulfuric acid from smelting sulfide ores.

sulfur in Canada

In Canada the recovery of sulfur as a by-product of natural gas began in 1951. By 1964 the output of sulfur from this source exceeded 1 million tons and further expansion is anticipated. The increase in elemental sulfur production has had several important consequences. As a result, less by-product sulfur from pyrites is being produced. Exports of sulfur are increasing rapidly and competing with or replacing sulfur shipments from the United States and Mexico, particularly in the Pacific markets.

Reserves of sulfur in sour natural gas in western Canada at the end of 1962 are estimated at 92 million short tons and experienced engineers have suggested that three times this amount may be found.

Although sulfur from sour gas is now the main source of supply, Canada also produces sulfur from pyrite. Pyrites cannot compete with sulfur for all markets but under conditions where sulfur dioxide, iron oxide residues, and other recoverable elements are attractive, pyrite may be produced.

Sulfur dioxide is also recovered from smelter gases to produce sulfuric acid, mainly at Trail, British Columbia, and Copper Cliff, Ontario.

Athabasca Oil Sand Sulfur

The occurrence of oil-bearing sand deposits along the Athabasca River in northern Alberta has been known since 1883. These sands contain extremely large quantities of oil with small but significant content of sulfur. In the event of the exploitation of the oil sands, since these sands contain 5 per cent of sulfur by weight, the sulfur would be recovered. Estimated oil reserves in the sands total more than 300 billion barrels and on this basis sulfur reserves would amount to more than 1 billion tons.

sulfur in Europe

France. Elemental sulfur is recovered in France from the natural gas production in the Lacq gas field in southwestern France. Beginning with an output of 28 tons in 1957, sulfur output rose to 1.5 million tons in 1963, making France an important world supplier. The major portion of exports, however, went to Western European nations: United Kingdom, West Germany, Netherlands, Belgium-Luxembourg.

Spain. The sulfur resources of Spain are in the form of iron pyrites. Her reserves are among the largest in the world. Most of the deposits occur in Huelva Province in southern Spain. Reserves have been estimated at about 250 million tons.

Poland. In 1960 Poland entered the list of sulfur producers through the opening of a sulfur deposit discovered in 1953. Production rose to nearly 300,000 tons in 1964 and further increases are anticipated.

An important but relatively unrecognized factor in the production of sulfur in many of the more than 30 nations reporting is the impact of increasing amounts of elemental sulfur derived from oil refineries, coke oven gases, zinc and copper smelters, and similar operations. These producers are generally small and serve local markets; none appear to supply significant amounts. However, they are producing sulfur on a world-wide basis and new plants are being built each year. The trend toward by-product sulfur recovery at oil refineries will probably continue, notably in Western Europe and in Japan, where oil consumption is rising rapidly.

sulfur in Asia

Iran has entered the list of producers from the gases of the large refinery at Abadan. Japan, the largest sulfur producer in the Orient, derives its supply mainly from pyrites, of which it is the world's leading producer. Also contributing to the sulfur supply are native sulfur deposits and recovered sulfur from refinery gases.

U.S.S.R. In the Soviet sulfur industry, pyrites are the most important source material. Next in importance is a large sulfur deposit in western Ukraine with an estimated reserve of 10 to 30 million tons of elemental sulfur. In the Soviet nonferrous smelters only partial recovery is achieved.

Chapter 8

Building Materials

In recent years demand for industrial minerals as building materials has grown rapidly, owing to a growing population and an even more rapid growth in per capita consumption of mineral products. Production of industrial minerals, especially those used for construction purposes, tend to be concentrated in or near urban centers. Low cost, high volume, widely occurring minerals tend to have high "place value"; that is, the location of the deposit with respect to the point of consumption is extremely important in determining which deposits are economical and can be utilized. Among the industrial minerals important to the building industry are cement, clays, gypsum, lime, sand and gravel, and stone.

cement

Portland cement concrete is the most widely used construction material in the world. In the United States almost twice as much concrete is used as all other structural materials combined. Raw materials needed in the manufacture of cement are clay or shale, and lime in the form of limestone, marl, or shells. Minor ingredients are magnesium carbonate, alumina, and iron oxide.

Portland cement has little utility alone but is the material which, in the presence of water, binds mineral aggregate into concrete. The early uses of concrete were for foundations, dams, piers, bridge abutments, and street paving, where compressive strength was the primary requirement. Many other uses were added when reinforcing steel was imbedded in the concrete to compensate for lack of tensile strength. Buildings of all sorts, residential, commercial, industrial and educational, are now being built of concrete.

Cement is manufactured in more than 90 nations. A domestic cement industry has become almost a prerequisite where industrialization is undertaken. One of the first needs of a developing nation or area is some form of transportatation. A concrete road for truck vehicles is probably the most practical. As a result, many under-developed nations have established cement industries.

gypsum

The most important, and continually expanding, market for gypsum is the construction industry. Wallboard, lath, sheathing, other board products, and ceiling tiles are the principal forms. Gypsum deposits of good quality occur in many states. All of the states in the Rocky Mountain area have substantial deposits. Extensive deposits are also known in California, Kansas, Nevada, Oklahoma, and Texas. In the midwest, Iowa, Indiana, Michigan and Ohio are the principal sources, and in the east, New York and Virginia are producers. In foreign nations gypsum is widely available and most nations are able to obtain their needs from their own resources.

sand and gravel

There are more than 5000 active producers of sand and gravel in the United States. Total volume exceeds that of any other mineral commodity. Production is reported from every state and deposits are located in almost all counties. Extensive use of sand and gravel in concrete for construction of buildings and bituminous paving accounts for 96 per cent of total production. Other uses of sand are in glass manufacture, molds for castings, in ceramics, fillers, abrasives, and the like. The production of nearly 1 billion tons of sand and gravel, most of which is used in metropolitan areas, has reduced supplies near some large cities to the point where these supplies must be secured from greater distances with accompanying higher costs.

stone

Of the three divisions of the stone industry, dimension stone, slate, and broken and crushed stone, only the last named is of importance. The first two make up a small part of the stone industry and are declining in output.

Crushed and broken stone, a basic construction, chemical and metallurgical raw material, is a major commodity in both tonnage and value.

Limestone is the most important rock, accounting for about 70 per cent of the total crushed stone production. Large quantities of basalt, granite, and quartzite or sandstone are also used. Domestic reserves are large, but stone deposits of the character or quality required to meet specifications for a particular use are limited in some areas. Metallurgical or chemical-grade stone is a special case with definitely restricted distribution of deposits.

clay

Clay is produced in 48 states and the District of Columbia. Clays have a wide variety of uses in paper manufacture, rubber, pottery and stoneware, floor and wall tile, refractory uses, heavy clay products, iron ore pelletizing, and filtering uses.

Chapter 9

Gold, Silver and Platinum

The metal silver has come prominently to public attention with the crisis in the supply of silver coins and the need for a modification of coinage metal. The silver shortage has arisen from the fact that consumption for industrial and coinage uses has risen sharply, especially in the last decade, and new production has shown little growth. During this period the use of silver increased in all major industrial categories. The important uses for silver are in the manufacture of photographic materials, silverware and jewelry, electrical and electronic uses, brazing alloys and solders, and battery manufacture. The quantity of silver used in coinage in recent years prior to 1966 had also risen sharply, from 77 million ounces in 1962 to 320 million ounces in 1965. About 201 million Kennedy half dollars were minted using about 73 million ounces of silver. Coinage requirements of the United States constituted three-fourths of the total silver used in free world coinage.

Increases in demand for silver over current production were supplied by silver stocks of the United States Treasury. These consist of free silver bullion, bullion covering silver certificates, and silver dollars and subsidiary coin, both in the treasury and in circulation. Several actions were taken to meet the increased demand for silver.

In November, 1961, the treasury suspended the sales of silver to industrial users at $0.91 from its "free" or non-monetized silver stocks. Also in November, 1961, the President directed the treasury to retire $5 and $10 silver certificates, with additional Federal Reserve note issues filling the gap. While this action freed 250 million ounces of silver, both the rate of coinage and the demands of industry increased rapidly and depletion of treasury stocks continued. In 1963, the Federal Reserve Board was authorized to issue Federal Reserve notes of one dollar denominations to replace silver certificates in this denomination which at that time tied up over 1.3 billion ounces of silver for backing. Thus the authority to issue one dollar Federal Reserve notes provided much needed flexibility by making possible the retirement of silver certificates and freeing the silver reserves behind them. This made the treasury a residual supplier of silver for demand in excess of commercial offerings of silver. The price was fixed by the treasury at $1.293 an ounce.

These steps did not solve the problem of subsidiary coinage supply. Such supplies were already short in 1962 and became scarcer in 1963 and 1964. Coin use had been expanding rapidly, partly reflecting the widening use of vending machines, parking meters, toll roads, sales taxes, coin operated laundries, and similar things. Minting of silver coins was stepped up sharply, and by 1965 the shortage had been considerably alleviated. However, the amount of silver needed to make the required coins was far greater than anticipated. It became apparent that treasury stocks of silver would soon run out if output of coins of 90 per cent silver content continued.

To cope with the impending silver crisis, the treasury early in 1965 made several recommendations, which Congress accepted with few changes. The result was the Coinage Act of 1965, signed by the President on July 23, 1965. This Act provided for the following:

1. A new half dollar, a composite coin containing 40 per cent silver against 90 per cent in the former half dollar. Its silver content would not be worth its face value unless the price of silver rose to around $3.38 an ounce.
2. A new dime and a new quarter, also composite coins, containing no silver. The old dimes and quarters contain 90 per cent silver.
3. An unchanged silver dollar (containing 90 per cent silver), but specified that none shall be minted for five years from July 23, 1965. In addition, it authorized a Joint Commission on the Coinage to determine future silver and coinage policies.

the supply of silver

The leading silver producers in the world are Mexico, Peru, the United States, Canada, the U.S.S.R., Australia, and Japan. Together these seven nations account for four-fifths of the world's production. Seven other countries, Honduras, Bolivia, Chile, East Germany, Spain, Sweden, and the Republic of South Africa, produce more than 1 per cent each but less than 3 per cent of the world total. The remaining producers yield less than 1 per cent.

About two-thirds of the world's silver is mined as a by-product of lead and zinc, copper, or gold ores. The output of the metal, therefore, is largely influenced by the changes in output of the nonferrous metals with which it is associated rather than by a price incentive. In the United States, for example, two-thirds of the domestic silver output came as a by-product and the remainder came from ores in which silver was the principal product. Idaho is the leading silver producing state and has the *Sunshine mine,* the nation's largest silver producer. The four leading silver producing states are Idaho, Arizona, Montana and Utah, which together account for about 90 per cent of the output.

Mexico maintains a dominant position among the world's silver producing nations. Silver mines are located in the states of Durango, Chihuahua, Zacatecas, and Hidalgo. The metal is exported to the United States, the United Kingdom and Germany.

In *Peru* silver output parallels that of the United States. Cerro de Pasco accounts for nearly half of Peru's silver output. With one or two exceptions, all silver production is associated with lead and lead-zinc ores. The product of the mines is exported mainly, but not entirely, to the United States.

Canada ranks with Peru and the United States in silver output. The principal sources of silver are the lead-zinc and silver-lead-zinc ores, most of which are mined in British Columbia. Another important source is the copper, copper-nickel, and copper-zinc ores of Canada. A smaller quantity comes from silver-cobalt ores in northern Ontario. Among the provinces, the leading producer is Ontario, followed by the Yukon, British Columbia, and Quebec.

In the *Soviet Union* most silver is produced as a co-product of copper, lead, and zinc.

In *Australia,* all silver mined is associated with ores of other metals, primarily in the three lead-zinc districts: Broken Hill, New South Wales; Mt. Isa, Queensland; Reed-Rosebery, Tasmania. The metal is exported mainly to the United Kingdom.

Gold

Gold has played a significant and complex role throughout the history of man. Because of its attractiveness, durability, and suitableness for coinage, it is prized as an important storehouse of value. Gold is sought for a variety of reasons: by business for industrial or artistic purposes, by central bankers for additions to the monetary reserves of the nations of the world, and by individuals for hoarding purposes. The total supply of gold available to accommodate these various buyers comes from newly mined productions and from various sellers. In recent years the Soviet Union has been a source of gold to finance its purchases from Western nations.

About three-fourths of the gold used in industry is for jewelry, artistic, and dental uses; the remainder is used in electrical and electronic components, and in defense, aerospace, and other industrial equipment.

The chief use of gold continues to be in the monetary systems of the world. The principal holders of the world's monetary gold, exclusive of the U.S.S.R., are the United States, West Germany, France, Switzerland, the United Kingdom and Italy. In the United States monetary structure the standard unit of value, the dollar, is defined by statute as a weight of gold. Gold, however, is not coined into money and does not enter into public circulation or into private banks. Gold nevertheless functions as reserve money of the Federal Reserve Banks. It also functions as a means of settling international balances. Under the law, as originally written, the Reserve Banks must hold gold certificates as a reserve against their liabilities for notes and deposits, respectively. The legal minimum is 25 per cent. In 1965, at the request of the President, the legal reserve applied only to notes and excluded deposits. This had the effect of releasing approximately $4.5 billion and adding this to the sum that can be used to protect the dollar internationally. At the rate of expansion of Federal Reserve note issue in recent years, the 25 per cent limit will be reached in less than a decade. Reconsideration of the gold reserve requirements for domestic currency may be necessary. The reserve requirement is primarily a legacy of the days when the United States and other major nations were on a domestic gold standard in which currency and deposits could be converted into gold at the holder's request. In today's managed-money economy, the requirement has no effective influence over the amount of money.

Repealing the gold reserve requirement does not mean that the United States can cut loose from gold. Other nations do not want to demonitize gold by international agreement, giving up their official gold reserves and making gold merely a commodity traded on the markets. The United States must maintain a gold reserve to meet its international obligations. To release gold from its domestic reserve obligations means that the nation has an ample reserve for payments for claims from abroad.

sources of gold

The Republic of South Africa produces about 70 per cent of the world's gold output. Other moderately large producers are the Soviet

Union, Canada, the United States, Australia, Ghana, Rhodesia, the Philippines, and Colombia.

The increase in world output of gold is attributable entirely to South Africa. The mines are apparently reaching a peak production and will level off if not decline. Canada, the second largest of the free world producers, is also showing signs of declining gold output. In the United States, the Homestake mine in South Dakota is the leading producer. Utah, the second largest state in gold production, derives most of its output as a by-product of copper in the Bingham Canyon pit.

Platinum

The metals of the platinum group include platinum, palladium, iridium, osmium, rhodium, and ruthenium. Of these, platinum is by far the most important. The metal is used in the chemical industry where resistance to chemical attack and resistance to oxidation are special properties of utmost importance. Eight nations report production of the platinum metal group of which the leading ones, in order of importance, are the U.S.S.R., Republic of South Africa, and Canada, which together produce more than 95 per cent.

Chapter 10

Nuclear Fuels

Uranium

The use of uranium as a source of energy was ushered in on July 16, 1945, when the first man-made atomic explosion was achieved on the Alamogordo Air Base southeast of Albuquerque, New Mexico. In 1957, the first commercial reactor built by the Atomic Energy Commission went into action at Shippingport, Pennsylvania. Twenty years after the initial explosion in New Mexico there were 15 atomic plants operable with a capacity of 1,889,200 kw. and 26 plants under construction or proposed for completion by 1972 with a capacity of 16,178,900 kw.[1] Nuclear energy is obtained by splitting an isotope of the atom uranium (U-235) which comprises 0.7 per cent of the whole uranium. The remainder of the natural uranium is the non-fissionable isotope U-238. A flow diagram of the splitting (fissioning) of U-235 is shown in the following diagram.

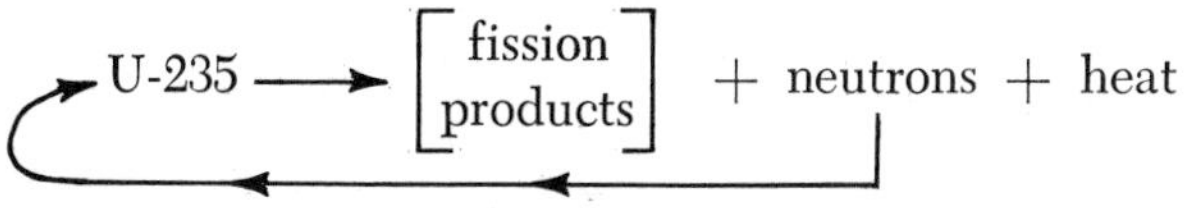

$$\text{U-235} \longrightarrow \begin{bmatrix}\text{fission} \\ \text{products}\end{bmatrix} + \text{neutrons} + \text{heat}$$

(neutrons return to U-235)

The neutrons released from the splitting of U-235 bombard other U-235 atoms and, under proper control, promote a sustained reaction with a continued release of heat energy. This, then, can be converted into electrical energy by conventional power plant equipment. Heat from fission instead of heat from coal can be used to generate steam. The energy released from 1 gram of U-235 is equivalent to the heat of com-

[1]Alderfer, E. B., "Electric Utilities Go Nuclear," *Business Review*, Federal Reserve Bank of Philadelphia, December, 1966, pp. 3-9.

bustion of 3 tons of coal.[2] The difficulty posed by the use of U-235 for power generation is its comparative scarcity. However, it has been found that the isotopes of U-238 and Th-232 (thorium) can be converted into fissionable materials. This is accomplished by placing U-238 in a "pile" originally powered by the fissionable U-235. This brings about a reaction which converts U-238 to plutonium (Pu-239) and Th-232 to U-233, both of which are fissionable. The process of converting U-238 or Th-232 into fissionable isotopes is known as "breeding." This process, if it can be achieved commercially, will add enormously to the available nuclear fuel.

The present quantity and distribution of reasonably assured reserves are given in Table 10.1. The listed tonnages represent reasonably assured reserves exploitable at \$5-\$10 per pound U_3O_8.

TABLE 10.1

Uranium Reserves

Country	Reserves, Tons U_3O_8
United States	160,000
Australia	10,000
Canada	210,000
France	40,000
South Africa, Republic of	150,000
Other Free World	50,000
Communist countries (except Yugoslavia)	Not available
Free World Total	620,000

thorium

Monazite, the source of thorium oxide, is imported from Australia, Malaysia, and Ceylon. Its principal uses are in magnesium alloys and gas mantle manufacture. Thorium is used experimentally as a fertile material in nuclear reactors to produce fissionable U-233.

lithium

Lithium compounds are recovered in North Carolina, Nevada, and California. These compounds are used in the production of the metal and alloys and also in the glass and ceramic industries.

---

[2]Hubbert, M. K., *Energy Resources,* Washington, D.C.: National Academy of Science, 1962, Publication 1000-D, p. 107.

Mineral Notes

Salt

Salt can be found in some form in nearly every country, and the world's resources are almost unlimited. Salt is essential in the human diet. In the main, it is a raw material used in the manufacture of such common chemicals as soda, sodium bicarbonate, caustic soda, and hydrochloric acid. Salt and its compounds are used in the manufacture of dyes, paper, cotton thread, and cements. Large areas of salt beds are located in Michigan, northern Ohio and western New York. The salt beds in south-central United States are the largest known deposits in the world. The area includes parts of New Mexico, Texas, Oklahoma, and Kansas, and is roughly 100,000 square miles in extent.

Mercury

The leading world producers of mercury are Spain, Italy, the United States, Mexico, Yugoslavia, and the communist countries. Domestic production is located principally in California and Nevada.

Feldspar

Feldspar is produced in North Carolina, California, South Dakota, and Arizona. Major uses of feldspar are glass, pottery, and enamel.

Cobalt

About half of the world's cobalt output is produced in the Congo (Kinshasa). Other significant producers are Canada, Morocco and Zambia. Cobalt is used in the manufacture of high-temperature, high-strength alloys, permanent magnets and alloy steels.

Boron

The entire domestic production of boron minerals is from Searles Lake brines in southern California. The principal foreign producer is Turkey. Principal uses for boron minerals and compounds are in glass products, soaps and detergents, enamels and fertilizers.

Tin

About half of the world's tin output is produced in the far eastern states of Indonesia, Malaysia, and Thailand. Other important producers are the Congo (Kinshasa) and Nigeria in Africa, Bolivia, and the U.S.S.R. Major uses for tin are for tinplating, solders, bronze and brass.

Barite

Barite is produced in eleven states, although two-thirds of the output comes from Arkansas and Missouri. The largest use, by far, for barite is as a weighting agent in oil and gas well drilling muds. It is also used in paints, glass and rubber.

Titanium

The two principal ores of titanium are *ilmenite* and *rutile*. Deposits of titanium ore minerals are widely scattered with major economic deposits found in Australia, Canada, Finland, India, Norway, Malaya, Sierra Leone, the Republic of South Africa, and the United States. Ilmenite is more abundant than rutile and is chiefly used in the manufacture of titanium oxide, a white pigment. The principal use of rutile is in the preparation of titanium metal. In Florida it is separated (along with zirconium) from beach sands.

Mica

Mica is produced in the form of sheets, scrap, and ground material. Sheet mica is used mainly in the electrical and electronic industries. Scrap mica is mined from pegmatite deposits; it is also a by-product of mining, trimming, and fabricating sheet mica. It is usually ground, and, with other sources of ground mica, is used as a filler and surface coating in roofing materials, wallboard, cements, paints, rubber, plastics and drilling muds. Nearly 80 per cent of the world's output of sheet mica is supplied by India. The United States is the leading producer of scrap mica. Other significant producers are Brazil, Norway, and the Republic of South Africa.

Water

Among mineral resources, water contributes, directly or indirectly, to the supplying of more human wants than does any other natural resource. It is an absolute necessity in the functioning of the human body, with regular daily supplies as important as foods. In varying degrees water is vital in all segments of economic activity. As the population grows and the plane of living is raised, the total demand for water increases through new uses and the intensification of old uses.

The most unique features of water supply are its cyclical replenishment in generally dependable recurring seasonal and annual patterns and its change of state from gas to liquid and back again in a continuous cycle. The supply of water is often deficient in relation to its numerous needs, and to the extent increasing needs cannot be offset by conservation measures this deficiency will become progressively more stringent.

The amounts and distribution of the annual water crop is the resultant of meteorological and other forces operating well beyond man's control. These are, mainly, the vaporizing power of the sun drawing water into the atmosphere, the space relation of water and land surfaces, the geographical differential in the absorption of the sun's rays, air-mass circulation, and the topography of land surfaces.

In its vapor state water is unmanageable, and programs for its conservation are restricted to its liquid form on or under the earth's surface. The quantity available for management is a residual after many deductions from the original amounts precipitated. The manageable water crop is usually only a small fraction of total precipitation.

Bibliography

General

American Institute of Mining, Metallurgical and Petroleum Engineers, *Economics of the mineral industry,* 2nd ed. A series of articles by specialists: New York: Am. Inst. Mining, Metall. Engineers, 1964, 787 pp.

U.S. Bureau of Mines, "Mineral facts and problems," U.S. Bur. Mines Bull. 630, 1965, 1118 pp.

Voskuil, W. H., "The search for mineral adequacy," *Jour. Geog.*, vol. 58, no. 8, 1959, pp. 385-399.

Iron

Angel, Tryggve, "The Lamco Iron Ore Development in Liberia," *Min. Cong. Jl.*, vol. 53, no. 1, January, 1967, pp. 69-72.

"Minas Gerais proved iron ore reserves reach 5 billion tons," *Eng. Min. Jl.*, vol. 166, no. 1, p. 96, 1965.

"Iron Ore in Chile, Brazil, Venezuela and Colombia," *Mining World,* vol. 22, no. 4, May, 1960, pp. 31-44.

Schuellman, G. A., "Iron Ore Reserves and the World's Changing Needs," *Optima,* vol. 16, no. 2, June, 1966, pp. 73-87.

"Australia: Iron Ore," *U.S. Bur. Mines, Min. Trade Notes,* vol. 62, no. 3, March, 1966, pp. 14-20.

U.S. Bureau of Mines, *Minerals Yearbook,* vol. IV, International, 1963 and 1964.

U.S. Steel Corp., The Making, Shaping and Treating of Steel, 8th ed., Pittsburgh, Pa.: U.S. Steel Corporation, 1964, 1300 pp.

Wilbur, J. S., "The World Iron Ore Situation, 1964," IV Latin American Iron and Steel Congress, Mexico City, July, 1964.

Coke and Alloying Materials

Risser, H. E., "Emerging patterns of coking coal supply," *Mines Mag.*, July 1958, (also Illinois State Geol. Survey reprint series 1958 S), 4 pp.

"Quick facts about alloy steels," 5th ed.: Bethlehem, Pennsylvania, Bethlehem Steel Co., 44 pp., 1964.

Coal

Averitt, Paul, 1961. "Coal Reserves of the United States and of the World," p. 5 in Domestic and World Resources of Fossil Fuels, Radioactive Minerals, and Geothermal Energy; Preliminary Reports Prepared by Members of the U.S. Geological Survey for the Natural Resources Subcommittee of the Federal Science Council.

Hubbert, M. King, "Energy Resources," National Academy of Sciences, National Research Council Publication 1000-D, 1962.

U.S. Bureau of Mines, "International Coal Trade," vol. 26, no. 8, 1957; vol. 26, no. 12, 1957; vol. 27, no. 4, 1958; vol. 28, no. 2, 1959; vol. 31, no. 11, 1962; vol. 32, no. 11, 1963; vol. 33, no. 9, 1964; vol. 33, no. 10, 1964; vol. 33, no. 12, 1964; vol. 34, no. 3, 1965; vol. 34, no. 5, 1965; vol. 34, no. 11, 1965; vol. 34, no. 12, 1965; vol. 35, no. 3, 1966; vol. 35, no. 5, 1966; vol. 35, no. 8, 1966; vol. 35, no. 9, 1966; vol. 35, no. 11, 1966; vol. 35, no. 12, 1966; vol. 36, no. 6, 1967.

"Mineral Trade Notes," *U.S. Bureau of Mines*, vol. 50, no. 3, Spec. Supp. No. 59, March, 1960.

Oil

"Proved Reserves of Crude Oil, Natural Gas Liquids, and Natural Gas," Amer. Petroleum Instit. (Pub. annually.) Vol. 21.

"Review of the mineral-fuel industries," *Minerals Yearbook, U.S. Bur. Mines*, vol. 2. (Pub. annually.)

Copper and Aluminum

Feiss, J. W., 1965, Copper: Rocky Mountain Minerals Conference, October, 1965; New York, Am. Inst. Mining Metall. Engineers, Soc. of Mining Engineers, preprint no. 65K328.

Lesemann, R. H., ed., "Copper Market Guide, 1965," *Eng. Mining Jour. Metal and Mineral Markets,* Oct. 25, 1965, pp. 5-54.

McMahon, A. D., "Copper, a materials survey," *U.S. Bur. Mines Inf. Circ. 8225,* 1965, 340 pp.

"Copper in Canada," *U.S. Bur. Mines Min. Trade Notes,* U.S. Bureau of Mines, 1964, vol. 58, no. 5, pp. 11-17.

Lead and Zinc

Callaway, H. M., "Lead, a Materials Survey," *U.S. Bur. Mines Inf. Circ. 8083,* 1962, 194 pp.

Gold and Silver

"Treasury Staff Study on Silver and Coinage," United States Treasury Department, 1965, 49 pp.

"A Study of Alloys Suitable for Use as United States Coinage," Battelle Memorial Institute: 1965, 46 pp.

Plant Foods

Beall, J. V., "Phosphate Rock in the United States, 1966," *Min. Eng.*, vol. 18, no. 10, Oct., 1966, pp. 80-99.

LEVITSKY, SERGE L., "Sulphur," *Min. Cong. Jl.*, vol. 52, no. 2, February, 1966, pp. 170-74.

"Potash in Saskatchewan," *Mining Jour.* (London), vol. 256, no. 6552, 1961, p. 303.

TEN EYCK, H. S., "The Multiple Problems Facing the Fertilizer Industry," *Mining Engineering*, vol. 19, no. 7, July, 1967, pp. 161-164.

TOMPKINS, R. V., "Canadian potash—the world's future supply of a vital mineral," *Canadian Mining Metall. Bull.*, vol. 55, no. 606, 1962, pp. 691-695.

WAGNER, R. E., "Potassium: What It Is and Where It Is Going," *Soc. Min. Eng.* Preprint No. 66H15, 1966, 15 pp.

Index